Vets School

VETS
SCHOOL
Grant Mansfield

BBC BOOKS

For James, Jenna, Harriet and George Edward

This book is published to accompany the television series entitled
Vets School which was first broadcast in 1996.

Executive Producer: Grant Mansfield
Series Producer: Nick Shearman

Published by BBC Books,
an imprint of BBC Worldwide Publishing,
BBC Worldwide Limited, Woodlands,
80 Wood Lane, London W12 0TT

First published 1996
© Grant Mansfield 1996
The moral right of the author has been asserted.

ISBN 0 563 38769 6

Designed by Andrew Shoolbred
All photographs by David Ward except those on pages 102, 103, 182 and 183,
which were taken by John Jefford.

Set in Meridien
Printed in Great Britain by Martins of Berwick Ltd, Berwick-upon-Tweed
Bound in Great Britain by Hunter & Foules Ltd, Edinburgh
Jacket printed by Lawrence Allen Ltd, Weston-super-Mare

Contents

Introduction 7

The cream *11*

Farm animals *23*

Small animals *45*

Horses *76*

Surgery *88*

Social life *98*

Charity work *106*

So you want to be a vet *129*

'Holidays' *137*

Job hunting *171*

Finals *179*

Index *190*

Acknowledgements

It wasn't easy writing a book in my 'spare time' and it would have been impossible but for the efforts and understanding of a large group of people. Above all, I would like to thank the staff and students at the Vet School and in particular Dr Kieran O'Brien, Alison Lee, Mike Sandiford, Jon Coupe, Fiona Green, Julie Richards, Steve Leonard and Trude Mostue.

Special thanks are due to Professor Philip Duffus, Head of the Vet School at Langford, who allowed our production team access to make the television series and also encouraged me to write this book. His advice, patience and sensitivity were invaluable.

Nick Shearman directed the series, identified the characters and did much to create the atmosphere of mutual respect and trust essential for a project of this kind. At BBC Books Sheila Ableman and Khadija Manjlai were generous with their support and advice. In the office my assistant Louise Jones organised and prioritised a heavy workload to accommodate the extra demands placed on us both by this book. And, at home, my children James, Jenna, Harriet and George Edward tolerated my extra absences and showed an understanding and interest which kept me going.

My thanks to all the above-mentioned people and my apologies to the many others who also helped but which space precludes me from mentioning here.

Introduction

TOMORROW'S VETS are today's brightest students. Only six universities in Britain run an undergraduate degree course in veterinary science and competition is so fierce that they can afford to be very choosy. The qualifications are three excellent A levels, preferably all at grade A. Some fortunate students might scrape in with two As and a B. Veterinary science is *the* most difficult degree course to get on. It is easier to become a doctor.

This book accompanies the BBC1 television series of the same name, which follows a group of students and staff during the final qualifying year at Bristol University. In fact they spend the last two years not in the city, but fourteen miles from Bristol in the village of Langford at the foot of the Mendip Hills. After three years of theory this is the time for their country practice.

Sixty-five students must abandon their busy social lives in one of the country's most favoured university cities and decamp to the edge of rural Somerset – swapping, as one put it, their shared Georgian flats in 'historic-happening Clifton' for 'digs in tiny villages with names like Nempnett Thrubwell'.

The move may signal the end of a 'happening' social life, but it also marks the beginning of the biggest challenge of their young academic lives. In particular, the students' final year provides a frenetic mix of classroom theory and hands-on practical experience.

Langford is like a general hospital, a microcosm of the veterinary world concentrated in one site. There is an intensive-care unit, a farm-animal practice, a new purpose-built small-animal hospital where local people bring their pets, an equine centre and five operating theatres. It

Professor Duffus with students Pat Ridge and Pippa Hughes in the milking chamber.

is in these surroundings that tomorrow's vets get to 'have a go' today. Unlike student doctors, they will have frequent opportunities to treat 'real' patients and sometimes to operate on them, too.

'The final months are deliberately designed to be stressful', according to the Head of the Veterinary School at Langford, Professor Philip Duffus. 'We want to challenge them, to see how and if they manage. After all, as soon as they leave they will immediately enter a very demanding and stressful profession. It's our duty to ensure they leave well prepared.' So, as well as coping with their studies, students must learn to deal with frightened and sick animals, emotional pet owners and demanding farmers.

As their finals approach the pressure grows. The young vets must try to juggle the twin and sometimes competing demands of caring for sick animals and revising for exams. It is a challenge that would defeat all but the most gifted. But because Bristol's students *are* among the most academically gifted young people of their generation, most will prove equal to the challenge. They will be helped along the way by an enormously committed teaching staff who comprise some of the best veterinary talent in the country, all of them specialists in their field.

'The skill of the teachers', says Professor Duffus, 'is to force the students into situations where they have to make critical decisions – but still under the umbrella of professional academic help so that if they make the wrong decision it is of no harm to the animals.'

At Langford the animals always come first, and not simply because staff and students are motivated by a personal desire to care for them. There are commercial reasons too. Horses, dogs, cats, cattle, sheep and pigs pay most of the bills – or at least their owners do. So Bristol's staff don't just teach. They sell their professional services as well. Of an annual budget of £10 million, only £3.5 million comes from the government and student fees. The other 65 per cent has to be earned through research and what is termed 'clinical income', fees paid by horse and pet owners and farmers. Not many university departments can claim to earn their keep in this way.

For the students, too, the economic realities of their chosen career become increasingly apparent as they progress through their last year at the veterinary school. Most describe themselves as 'animal lovers', but soon none will be under any illusion about the nature of that love. It cannot be unconditional and has to be tempered by economic realities.

Treatment costs money – sometimes too much money. Every animal has a price on its life. One of the toughest lessons for students is knowing that they could treat and save an animal, only to be confronted with an owner who says they can't or won't pay the bill. Putting an animal to sleep is often a question of cost.

Such life-and-death decisions are a far cry from the cosy academic theory of the first three years of the course. During their time in the lecture theatres in Bristol, students will have studied hard and learnt how to pass their exams. But once they're relocated and rehoused in rural Langford they must demonstrate an aptitude for the practical and an appetite for 'real' veterinary practice.

Can they handle a live animal or a livid owner? If they can't, they can be sure of only one thing – they will be found out in the final year.

For, during those crucial three terms, there is no hiding behind text-books and brilliant essays. This is the time when Britain's young academic elite discover whether they can hack it where it really matters. Not in classrooms but on farms, in surgeries and in operating theatres.

The challenge puts enormous pressure on students and, indeed, on staff, who are also judged by results. It is not an easy time to have a BBC film crew around, but we were always tolerated and usually welcomed. Inevitably, some individuals who were particularly welcoming were subjected to even closer attention and the dubious distinction of being invited to appear in our series – and this book! None of them sought this kind of exposure, but all were generous with their time and remarkably tolerant of our presence during some of their most stressful moments. This is their story.

The cream

'YOU ARE THE CREAM.' Four words intended to galvanise the 65 veterinary students who have slogged through four years of one of Britain's most demanding university courses. It is October, and they are now about to embark on their fifth and final year. It will be the toughest 25 academic weeks of their young lives.

Professor Philip Duffus, Head of the Veterinary School at Langford, near Bristol, makes no attempt to disguise his admiration for his pupils. 'They are the cream, very clever and incredibly highly motivated. It's a pleasure and a privilege to teach them. They are winners.'

The praise is fulsome – but the expectations are commensurate, and inevitably this brings extra pressures. '"Loser" is a very bad word here at Langford,' says Trude Mostue. 'I wish we could escape all this stuff about being the cream. All the lecturers try to reinforce it from day one and it only adds to the stress. I'm worried that as we get closer to our finals in June people are really going to crack up.'

At 28 Trude is one of the oldest students on the course. She is a physically striking woman whose long blonde hair and pronounced accent betray her Norwegian origins. Until she began the course in Bristol four years ago she had never been to England. Refreshingly open and occasionally outspoken, Trude readily admits that she has struggled to survive in such a competitive and, initially, alien environment.

Her English is now fluent in most situations, but it wasn't always that way. Recalling her arrival in this country, she compares her command of the language to a British person moving to Paris with O-level French. 'It was very tough', she says. 'If you can imagine going into a biochemistry lecture on day one and thinking the only thing I can really say is "Hi, I'm Trude", then you may get an idea of the challenge I faced.'

Trude failed her first year on the course and had to resit the exams. She has been under constant pressure ever since, marked out as a student who may not make the grade. But she has never contemplated giving up and going home. Against the expectations of some, she has survived to face the final year and is now within striking distance of the coveted veterinary degree.

She is realistic in her goals, knowing that she will never be top of the class. Her age also means that there is a certain distance between her and the other students, but her greater maturity also helps her keep things in perspective.

Trude's focus is not on competing with the other aspiring vets but simply on passing. An honours degree is beyond her – and she knows it – but that doesn't matter as long as she does just enough to qualify. 'I know I'm not going to get the best marks, so I won't be on the front row on graduation day. But I don't need to be on the front row to make a good vet. My parents might have to look a little harder to spot me in the graduation line-up, but I'll be there.'

However, some of her lecturers aren't so sure. Indeed, at least one of them is predicting that she may fall at the final hurdle. Dr Kieran O'Brien is the forthright and fiery head of the large-animal practice. It is his job to help students acquire farm animal and equine skills. He doesn't mince his words. 'Trude doesn't know the answer to a lot of very simple things. And although I am encouraged by the fact that she remains positive and determined to improve things, I still think she'll fail.'

If Trude does fail, she will be in good company. At 52, Professor Duffus is one of Britain's leading veterinary figures. His research on immunology is internationally renowned and, before becoming Head of the Bristol Veterinary School at Langford, he was deputy head of the school at Cambridge. Clever, personable, diplomatic and highly regarded, it is easy to appreciate his rise to the top of his profession.

It is surprising, therefore, to discover that the career of Philip Duffus began with an embarrassing hiccup. Thirty years ago, in the class of '66 at the Liverpool Veterinary School, he contrived to fail his finals. He qualified only after resitting all his exams.

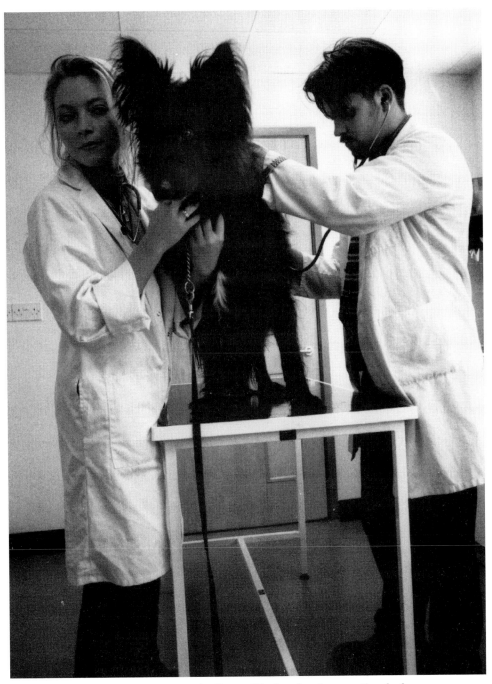

Students Trude Mostue and Mike Sandiford performing a routine check-up.

Professor Duffus doesn't expect many of his students to fail, but reckons that those who do should take heart from his story. All of them have heard it but, even so, few can bear to contemplate failure. It is not in their nature – a characteristic that is both a strength and a weakness.

The competition for places is much tougher now than it was when Philip Duffus was a student. Britain's six veterinary schools offer only 400 places annually and, while some of the students certainly resent the 'academic cream' tag, it is a fact that each school can pick and choose the most gifted students.

Because it is the toughest degree course to get on, those that make it arrive with an outstanding record of academic achievement. They are used to being top of the class at almost everything, and they expect it to continue. They are in for a shock.

'The students have grown accustomed to getting As in everything,' says Kieran O'Brien, 'so they have great difficulty when we start giving

Jon Coupe in the intensive-care unit.

them Bs and even Cs. They'll complain to me, saying "I've always been an A student". When they were at school they would get 80 per cent at everything, whereas we almost never give any more than 60 per cent in anything. It takes a while to get used to that.'

'It's very competitive,' says Trude Mostue, 'and there's a strong sense that you shouldn't show your weaknesses. Most of the students here are used to being head and shoulders above their classmates throughout their school life. Then suddenly, when they arrive here, they're thrown into a situation where everyone is bright and able.'

Trude is not alone in worrying about the huge emphasis on academic excellence. Fellow student Jon Coupe is outspoken in his criticism. 'All this constant talk about us being the cream is elitist, irritating nonsense. There's a great deal of academic snobbery here, a lot of it promoted by the teaching staff.'

Jon is 22 but looks older, courtesy of a fashionable goatee beard. He has spent four years cultivating an image as a hard-drinking cynic who knows how to do just enough to get by. His manner is direct and his forthright views are delivered with a distinctive Nottinghamshire accent. He is proud of his roots and wants to return to the City of Nottingham to practise once he has qualified.

Jon has dreamed of being a vet since he was a young boy. 'I've never wanted to be anything else. We always had lots of animals at home – little fluffy things, guinea pigs and gerbils, dogs and ponies.' His determination to be a vet was a big motivating factor at school. He knew he had to be an excellent pupil to stand any chance of being accepted on a veterinary degree course. So he worked very hard, particularly for his A levels. That level of commitment, he confessed, has not been maintained throughout his first four years at the Bristol Veterinary School. 'I've done just enough to get by since I got here. No more, no less. To be honest, I studied much more during the sixth form. I've eased off quite a bit since I got accepted for university.'

Jon is now a fierce critic of the entry system. He believes that the emphasis on outstanding academic achievement as the only passport to a career as a vet is a mistake. He claims it encourages the wrong kind of students – people who, unlike him, have no sense of vocation. Over a short lunch break in the vet school bar he chain-smokes, sips beer and outlines his concerns.

'The entrance qualifications here don't make sense', he says. 'You need three As or a minimum of two As and a B, and what you get is a lot of academics who are obviously very clever but are not going to be very good vets.'

Understandably, Jon won't name names but says that everyone in the school knows who they are 'and they know who they are'. His concern is those that get excluded. 'You've got people on three Cs who could easily do the work on the course and might be much more practically minded or have a real desire to be a vet.'

Dr Kieran O'Brien also has reservations about the entrance system – but even bigger reservations about its chief student critic. Jon Coupe is not his favourite student, and the analysis is scathing. 'He is a particular species I would identify as a rather frivolous sort of boozing rugby-playing guy. Because I myself was never one of the boozing rugby-playing types, I've never really identified with that kind of person.'

What O'Brien does identify with, though, is the concern that concentrating on outstanding A-level results could, in some cases, attract academics who may lack vocational or even intellectual substance. He should know since he is a member of the selection panel.

Seated in his cramped, tidy office with a picture of his favourite hunting hounds above his desk, Dr O'Brien expands on his views, which he recognises are bound to be regarded as contentious by other staff. It is something he has thought about a great deal, having been involved in the admissions procedure for several years. What the selection panel is aiming to do, he says, is to skim off the intellectual cream. In other words, those who get high grades.

O'Brien concedes that it is an enviable position for any university department, being able to choose from Britain's brightest young students. But he has real concerns, too. 'I think it can be a fairly blunt instrument because when I see them at the other end and they're just about to qualify it's clear there is quite a wide range of aptitudes, both intellectual and motivational. Some are good, but a surprising number show indifference and will leave here and be very average vets.'

Dr O'Brien, a large-animal specialist, is a controversial figure among the students. He is a feared but inspirational teacher and capable of being a particularly harsh critic. The fact that he loves to hunt has also done little to endear him to some of the people he teaches, though he insists it is a country pursuit that conveniently reflects both his love of horses and his need to form social ties with farmers, who are some of the veterinary school's most important clients.

Nevertheless, many of the students privately voice their dislike of O'Brien's methods and his personality. Some, like Jon Coupe, go public: 'I don't like horses and I don't like Kieran. He's a stuck-up upper-class git, basically.'

However, leaving aside the obvious enmity between O'Brien and Coupe, there is a consensus among staff and students that the concentration on academic excellence has fundamentally changed the kind of person that is being attracted into the profession.

It is a shift acknowledged by Professor Duffus, whose own career has spanned the period of change. He recognises that tomorrow's vets are coming from very different backgrounds to those of yesterday's vets. When he began 30 years ago most of the students came from a rural environment and had grown up surrounded by animals. It has all changed dramatically from when Duffus was an undergraduate.

'We now take a lot more people from urban backgrounds. They're bright, sure, but they have very little experience of animals. Some students are almost too frightened to pick up a cow's foot. I've even known some who are frightened of approaching a budgie.'

Steve Leonard, aged 22, is definitely not one of those. At six foot three and with short, cropped hair, he is an imposing physical presence. Not the sort to be frightened by budgies – though he does admit to a fear of horses, which he describes as 'evil, bad-tempered creatures'.

Generally, though, Steve exudes an easy-going charm and confidence around both animals and people, which has even endeared him to Kieran O'Brien. 'Steve Leonard is a really nice guy. He will be a first-class vet. Charming personality and genuinely interested in the things that I teach. He's that rare combination, being both clever and practical.'

So how did Steve Leonard cast his spell on the much-feared Dr O'Brien? 'On the first day we met him everyone was calling him Dr O'Brien or they just didn't call him anything at all. So I said, what do you want to be called? And he really appreciated that and asked

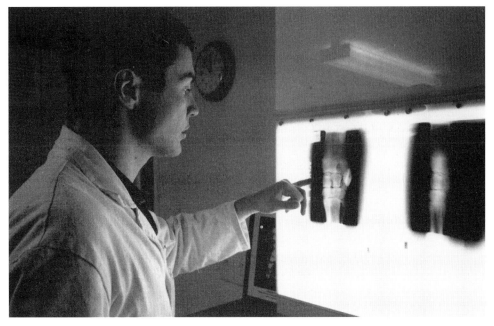

Steve Leonard checking X-rays.

me to call him Kieran. We've got on well ever since, which is quite rare.'

Steve's popularity and confidence undoubtedly owe much to his background. He is one of those unusual students who do have strong veterinary links. Very strong. His father and his two older brothers are all vets.

However, while he may always have had veterinary science in his blood, Steve also needed a good brain in his head. 'I cruised through school, and so did all my brothers and all my friends. It was just a matter of turning up, virtually. But then you turn up here and suddenly you're in the bottom third. There are just so many people who are more intelligent than you and you begin to think, maybe I'm not up to this.'

In fact he most certainly is up to it, one of the veterinary school's best students and expected to get his degree with ease – possibly with honours. Given his background, it is no surprise to hear him, too, question the emphasis on academic excellence. However, the last four years seem to have reassured him that the system is not badly flawed.

Steve remembers that when he first arrived he was convinced that some of the students had chosen the wrong course – or the course had chosen the wrong students. They were academics and would never acquire the necessary practical skills. 'I thought you had to have a kind of rustic, rugged background. But in fact it isn't true. If you're clever enough to be a vet, you're probably good enough to be a vet.'

Many schools would agree. There is certainly evidence that an increasing number of able children are being targeted for places on veterinary courses from a young age. They are encouraged to think about becoming vets simply because they are top of the class. These days it is a cachet for a school to get a pupil accepted for a veterinary degree.

Professor Duffus doesn't regard this approach to the choice of a degree course as a particular problem. He believes that perhaps as many as 25 of his 66 final-year students will not use their degree qualification for a long-term career in veterinary practice. It doesn't bother him because he maintains that they will have had a superb education, which they can put to good use as 'high flyers' in other professions. All employers know how difficult it is to get accepted at veterinary school, and that makes the students sought-after commodities in careers as diverse as industry, research and law.

'I think if the hardest course to get on to in the country was oriental studies, some of the same bright pupils might be pushed in the direction of that degree', he concedes. Dr O'Brien agrees with his boss. 'For many students, veterinary science is not a vocation but simply an aptitude. I don't think many of them have had a burning desire to be a vet since the age of four.'

It may be true but, understandably, few of the students are prepared to admit that they are not motivated by a genuine desire to care for animals. Fiona Green, in particular, doesn't care for cynicism about her motivation – indeed, she positively bridles at the suggestion. One of her lecturers had the temerity to suggest that anyone who liked animals shouldn't be a vet. Fiona's view on that? 'Bollocks. You've got to love the animals, otherwise there is no way you would do it. It's not a fluffy, unrealistic, aren't-they-cute love, it's a genuine interest.'

Fiona shoots from the hip and speaks from the heart. At 26 she is one of the older students, and her story is one of academic excellence combined with a real and persisting ambition to become a vet. School was a breeze until she was 16. She knew she wanted to be a vet from an early age and happily acknowledges her earliest influence.

'Everyone says James Herriot doesn't make a difference', she laughs. 'Well, I'm here to tell you that James Herriot bloody does make a difference.' She was brought up in a cathedral city in Staffordshire – a childhood, she says, which was hardly likely to provide her with the inspiration to become a vet. Then she discovered Herriot's best-selling veterinary tales, and that was it. 'His books introduced me to a world I knew nothing about and I liked what I read. It's one of the reasons I'm here today.'

Fiona's future appeared to be mapped out. She was highly motivated and smart enough to make the grade. But at sixteen, just before she sat her O levels, tragedy struck when a much-loved older brother was killed in a car crash. 'I couldn't concentrate after that,' she recalls, 'and somehow got diverted from the career which I had set my heart on.'

What followed was a long academic detour, which included four years studying at Oxford University. However, Fiona could not get veterinary science out of her mind. So, aged 22, she finally applied for a place at the Bristol Veterinary School. She was accepted, by now four years older than most of the other students.

Like all of them, Fiona displays a steely determination and an extraordinary capacity for hard work. Both qualities will be much needed in the final year. 'I worry about passing – everyone does', she admits, 'but in my heart of hearts I think I'll make it because I'm prepared to give everything.'

In a typical year a significant number of students will choose to use their degree as a passport to another career. Fiona is extremely unlikely to be one of them, although the statistics do provide ammunition for those who question the commitment of some of the students to veterinary practice. Professor Duffus estimates that, on average, 35 per cent will eventually tread a different career path.

However, not even the closest observer or the harshest critic could question the commitment of the students to their education. It still surprises Duffus, although it is now three years since he was appointed Head of the Veterinary School at Langford. 'I'm always amazed by the

Fiona Green on ward rounds in the intensive-care unit, accompanied by her own dog, Dotty (left). Many students have their own dogs throughout their final year.

amount of time they're prepared to set aside for their education. They think nothing of spending all their waking hours learning. They're even tied up with veterinary work in their holidays. This strikes me as laudable – but abnormal – student behaviour.'

It may well be that it is this 'abnormality' that curdles the academic cream. It does not rise effortlessly to the top. All the students at Bristol, no matter how naturally gifted, have had to work extremely hard to get on to the course and then make it through the first four years.

'I don't think any of us here are more intelligent than students in other places', insists Trude Mostue. 'I think we are just more committed. We work harder than any other students I know.'

During the three terms leading up to their finals, the 66 students at Bristol will have to work harder than at any time before. 'I'm already completely knackered and horribly behind with my work', complains Fiona Green. Jon Coupe is beginning to worry about not putting in more effort since arriving at university: 'I regret not working harder because I now have a hell of a lot of work compared with the people who have worked consistently hard throughout the course'. Steve Leonard is more confident. 'Occasionally I get bouts of worry, but I think I'll be able to do it really. I'm not saying that I'm not going to work, but I'm confident that I'm going to pass because I've got two brothers who passed before me.'

Undoubtedly, though, the person who has most cause to worry is Trude Mostue. For her it really is going to be a struggle to the end. She knows she has the dubious distinction of being one of the favourites to fail. Her response to the growing pressure has been to persuade her parents to pay for her membership at an expensive private health and fitness club. 'I'm not going to crack up. When I feel really stressed I go to the gym and chill out. It calms me down. I have to stay cool. After all,' she remarks, pausing for maximum ironic effect, 'that's the best temperature for cream!'

Farm animals

THE HANDS-ON PRACTICAL EXPERIENCE that the students have been promised begins as soon as they return from their summer holidays for the start of the Christmas term. It is called 'clerking' and will be the focus of most of their activities during the fifth and final year. The students regard it as both enormously demanding and incredibly rewarding. They recognise that the system is designed to test them where they are weakest. For the first time textbooks take second place as veterinary theory is tested in practice. From now on, three-quarters of their time will be spent outside the classroom.

Clerking is actually a series of clinical rotations that move students on and off the Langford campus in pursuit of the practical skills they must acquire. On the veterinary school site they will spend weeks working in the small-animal hospital, the large-animal practice, the equine centre and in surgery. Outside, there will be opportunities to 'have a go' on farms, in the PDSA, the People's Dispensary for Sick Animals, and at the RSPCA, the Royal Society for the Prevention of Cruelty to Animals. During holidays they will be attached to a private practice near their home.

Most of this experience will be gathered under the watchful eye of Bristol's specialist teachers. The students will be expected to demonstrate both knowledge and manual dexterity on live animals. They will not be allowed simply to stand back, watch the specialist and take notes. In fact it is the other way round. For the first time a teacher will be making notes about the student, awarding marks for what they do rather than an essay they might have written.

Tomorrow's vets will be expected to carry out fertility examinations on cattle, treat mastitis, deal with life-threatening cases of colic in horses and vaccinate kittens and puppies. They will also get the opportunity to acquire some surgical skills, performing operations to spay RSPCA animals. That can be a particularly nerve-racking experience – the first time they will take scalpel to skin.

Professor Duffus is a big fan of the clerking system, which, he believes, is essential to ensure that students can step straight out of veterinary school into veterinary practice. He says it tests gifted academic students in a way they've not been tested before. Up until the final year they have never really had to take a lot of responsibility on their young shoulders. Suddenly all that changes, a daunting experience for students who've grown comfortable in the classroom environment.

'They're used to sitting down and taking a whole lot of notes from an expert spouting on about anatomy or surgery or medicine', says the Head of the Langford Veterinary School. 'Then they simply regurgitate it in their exams. They are good at that. But what sort of education is it? What clerking does is to force them to confront real situations where they have to make real decisions – often immediately.'

It is no surprise, therefore, to learn that Duffus intends to strengthen the role of clerking in the syllabus. At the moment students spend three weeks clerking, followed by a week in the classroom. However, the current batch of fifth-year students will be some of the last to attend any formal lectures. The academic year beginning in October 1996 will be turned over almost entirely to clerking rotations.

Many of the current fifth-year students believe they are facing the prospect of a particularly tough time. Their year will be a transitional one, the first step in a move completely away from the theoretical to the practical. It is a move that they applaud. However, few of them are happy with the consequences of being caught up in what they see as a very demanding halfway house.

Fiona Green is one of the most outspoken critics. The previous crop of fifth-years had a much easier time, she says, because they had a fifty/fifty split between classroom and clerking. The problem she has identified for the current final-year students is that although they only spend half as much time in the classroom, they are still expected to cover as much academic work. 'Next year, when the school moves over to clerking full time, they won't have to bother with so much academic stuff. But we're caught in the middle of the change and I don't

Hands-on practice is vital for students at Langford. Above, lambing problems.

think the clinicians have any idea how hard it is. There's no time to shop or wash or do anything outside your work. It's horrendous.'

While they are clerking, the students are undergoing continuous assessment. It is not sufficient just to pass their exams in surgery, medicine and public health at the end of the course. They must also get a pass mark on each of their rotations if they are to be awarded a degree in veterinary science. Bristol's increasing emphasis on a more practical approach is a recognition that students who are good at passing exams are not necessarily going to make good vets.

'Didactic teaching isn't the best way to train vets', says Professor Duffus. 'You could pass a theory exam on how to drive a car without ever getting behind the wheel. But it isn't until you get behind the wheel that you discover whether you can actually drive a car.'

While the essential truth of the analogy may not be in doubt, an accident imbues it with a rather humorous irony. Sitting in a deserted canteen on a dark winter afternoon, Trude Mostue is nervously contemplating the challenges posed by her clerking rotation on the large-animal practice. But she is also particularly irritated with the man who is in charge of the practice, Dr Kieran O'Brien. 'I'm cross with him, very cross', she says. Why? He has just reversed his car into hers. It was an accident of course, but as O'Brien and Trude are not part of a mutual admiration society, it is an inauspicious start.

Dr O'Brien is predicting further trouble ahead. Not car trouble, but clerking trouble. A week visiting local farms beckons and the Head of the Small-Animal Practice makes some typically blunt observations. 'Trude Mostue suffers from a problem that when she's in a group situation she is very shy and her mind goes blank.'

He recounts a story concerning a horse, his favourite animal. He had been talking to Trude about preventing tetanus. If a horse has a wound it is very susceptible to tetanus and there is a very simple preventative measure, which apparently Trude was not aware of. O'Brien delivers the damning conclusion to the story with scarcely disguised incredulity. 'She didn't even know about giving a horse an injection, which is just mind-numbingly stupid.'

Such outspoken criticism is par for the course for the Irish academic, who openly admits that 'if I feel the students need bollocking I will do so in a fairly forthright manner, whereas many of my colleagues of a more Anglo-Saxon temperament may be more diplomatic.'

Trude knows the score and reasons that the problem might be temperamental – she a cool Norwegian, he a fiery Irishman. 'Kieran has got his favourites and I am not really one of them. He doesn't make any real attempt to get to know people, and though he can be a very good teacher he is also very intimidating.' She pauses for a second to reflect on his criticism before delivering some of her own. 'I'll tell you what Kieran's problem is. He doesn't have the ability to differentiate between people who are stupid and people who are simply shy.'

Kieran O'Brien has aroused strong feelings ever since he arrived at Langford in 1987. He began his career in a large-animal practice in Lancashire before doing his Ph.D. at the Cambridge Veterinary School when Philip Duffus was the deputy head there. O'Brien loves academic life, but he wasn't drawn to it for the teaching – a fact that may not surprise some of the students who undergo his 'bollockings'.

'I don't think people work in the vet school because they have a mission to teach', he argues. 'I enjoy the environment of a vet school, access to resources and facilities and an opportunity to work in a veterinary environment which is not driven strictly by commercial pressures. If you have an inquiring mind, it is very satisfying. As it happens, I enjoy teaching, but that isn't the reason I came.'

O'Brien is well aware of his reputation around the veterinary school and appears rather to enjoy it. To suggest that he deliberately courts controversy would perhaps be to overstate his approach, but he certainly doesn't shy away from it. He is a complex personality, hard for the students to fathom at times, but very keen to 'get some inter-action going'.

In a characteristically frank admission he says 'I am desperate not to appear bland, so I will deliberately say things sometimes to wind up the students'. It appears to work. Some talk about his dislike of vege-tarians, others of his contempt for those with left-wing political views – and one student even mentioned that he was appalled by women who don't shave their armpits! O'Brien laughs at these suggestions. 'I don't really dislike vegetarians and socialists or any "types" of people, though I'm fond of telling my students that I do.'

And what about those 'bollockings'? He is unapologetic, arguing that it is not in his nature to be diplomatic, and insisting that the stu-dents are tough enough to take it. 'Instead of saying, "If you don't do that I will be very cross with you", I am more likely to say, "If you don't get that right I'll kick your arse down to Windhurst Farm" – which is half a mile down the road.'

'The thing is that he's a man who says things off the cuff', says Steve Leonard, one of his favourite students. 'If you take everything on board it can really hurt you. Sometimes you'll give him an answer and he'll just turn round and say, "That's bollocks". You just have to ignore it because actually he is a very good teacher.'

Trude Mostue doesn't dispute O'Brien's skills, just his methods. Her week on large-animal practice begins on Monday morning with a lesson on how to trim cows' feet – or, to be more precise, their hooves. It is one of those apparently simple practical tasks that is in fact deceptively difficult.

Cows' hooves regularly overgrow, and when that happens they are susceptible to all sorts of infection. On a typical farm a third of the cows will go lame each year, a condition that is often preventable simply by trimming. So, though it is a tricky skill for young veterinary students to acquire, it is undeniably important that they master it

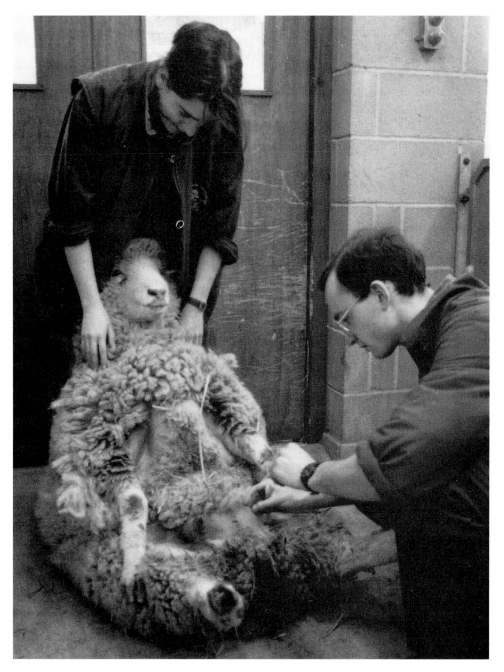

'Just lie back and relax.' A sheep being examined by students
Hannah de Boyne Pollard and Steve Benton.

before completing their course. Foot trimming will be a routine procedure for any of them working on farms in the future.

'It's a manual skill which many of the students find extremely difficult to get to grips with', says Kieran O'Brien. 'There are many things in veterinary science which look easy until you get to have a go. The students suffer from what I call "knife and fork syndrome". The knife we use is a specialist, precision tool, and you're not supposed to hold it like a piece of cutlery. A lot of them are cack-handed.'

With that in mind, training begins in a post-mortem room. The students must first practise on the feet of dead cattle. The veterinary school cannot afford significant mistakes when its pupils are let loose on a farm. The animals are not merely teaching aids. Much more importantly, they are a farmer's livelihood. And, as the farmer pays for the services offered by Langford, he has a right to expect them to be professional.

The service provided to local farmers by Bristol's qualified specialists brings much-needed additional income to the school. So the bottom line for Dr O'Brien is financial. The farmers are paying for high-quality veterinary care. If they do not get it the money will disappear and, with it, invaluable practical experience for aspiring vets.

It is for this reason that O'Brien insists that all his pupils and his staff understand their place in the practical pecking order. 'In terms of priorities, teaching must always come second. Students get to have a go, but it is our responsibility to ensure the job is done properly.' Frequently that means the qualified vet has to step in and take over. Farmers do not keep animals to entertain and educate students. 'They are making a living out of it,' says O'Brien, 'but if we plan things carefully we can bolt on a lot of teaching to their activities.'

For the farmers there is a financial incentive to sign a contract with the veterinary school. In return for allowing students the opportunity to examine and treat their livestock, they are charged a considerably reduced fee. It is less than half what they would pay in the commercial world, so the arrangement works for everyone.

Trude Mostue's other big challenge down on the farm will be to carry out fertility examinations on cattle – another routine but tricky task. 'It's basically hands up backsides', explains O'Brien. 'When you put your hand in there it's like putting your hand into an oil drum full of guts. The first difficulty is finding what you're supposed to be feeling, and the second is interpreting what you're supposed to be feeling.'

Mistakes are commonplace: 'I once took four students to examine two cows, one of which was about to give birth in two weeks while the other one wasn't even in calf. The one that was pregnant had a calf inside her as big as a person. They all got it the wrong way round.'

It is a few days after Christmas and freezing cold as Trude begins her first week visiting a group of farms located around the Mendip Hills. 'It's too cold for even a Norwegian', she complains to fellow student Mike Sandiford. For the moment, though, they are both warm, seated in the back of a Land Rover that is being driven by their teacher for the day, John Huxley.

John is one of Dr O'Brien's staff, a young houseman not much older than Mike and younger than Trude. Indeed, last year he was still a student at the London Veterinary School. Now, in a rapid reversal of roles, he is providing the tuition.

It is a short three-mile drive from the Langford campus to the farm – little time for small talk, but enough for both students to be bombarded with questions. John appears to have adapted to his new role with ease and not a little relish. He is constantly checking how much Mike Sandiford and Trude Mostue really know. When staff speak of a system of continuous assessment, they do mean continuous. As finals approach there is no let-up at all in the pressure.

The farm is on top of a hill – bleak, windy, cold and very muddy. When they arrive the three young veterinary students swap their shoes for wellies and put on some heavy-duty overalls. Trude wears a black hat to keep her long, plaited hair out of her eyes. They squelch off through the mud in the direction of a dingy cow shed. It is a dirty job, and about to get a lot dirtier.

John pauses for a brief chat with the farmer, who smiles at the students in a manner which suggests he has a better idea of what lies ahead than they do. 'We've got a couple of fertilities to do,' says John, 'and two cows' feet to trim.'

The cows have been tethered in a stall in preparation for their examination. John leads the students into the shed and without further preamble turns to Trude and Mike. 'This cow was seen by

Dr O'Brien a couple of weeks ago when she had a cyst on her right ovary. What the farmer wants to know is whether she's pregnant now. So, basically, it's hands up backsides time. We just need to have a feel and find out what's going on. Who wants to start?'

Silence. In the absence of a volunteer John chooses one. 'Trude, do you want to put the gloves on first?' It is a rhetorical question and not an attractive one for a student who has already decided she is happiest in cleaner and more controlled environments. Trude has a preference for small-animal practice and prefers to operate in consultation rooms with pets and their owners.

The 'glove' she is now unravelling more closely resembles a stocking. It has to, for these examinations are more about arms up backsides than hands. Trude soon has a large part of her arm inside 'the large oil drum' Dr O'Brien spoke of. She is concentrating hard and looking increasingly puzzled as John Huxley and Mike Sandiford look on. This is more of a hands-in experience than a hands-on one. Already it is clear that a 'routine' fertility check is going to be very tricky. It is obviously difficult to conduct an examination that relies on feel alone, particularly when the sense of touch is deadened by a glove. At least the cow doesn't seem

Arms up backsides. Student Emma Milne prepares for a fertility examination on a cow.

bothered. She is standing perfectly still, apparently unperturbed by the inexperienced fingers now groping around her insides.

After several minutes Trude concedes defeat. She says she is finding it impossible to locate either of the ovaries. John tries and, after a few moments, succeeds. He discovers that the cow's uterus has become 'skewed to the right'. Now he understands Trude's difficulties. 'That's probably why you got confused', he says encouragingly.

The cow isn't pregnant, so Mike Sandiford has the more straightforward job of injecting a drug which should make her fertile in 48 hours' time. This means that the farmer will know exactly when to artificially inseminate her.

Mike is clearly more comfortable in the farm environment than Trude. Now they move out of the comparative warmth of the shed into the yard, where the temperature is down to freezing. It is time to trim the cows' feet. This time Mike goes first, handling the animal with confidence and, helped by some gentle prompting from John Huxley, the job is completed in a few minutes.

While Trude prepares to do the same job on a different cow Mike talks about why he is happiest out and about on farms. He reckons it is a good combination for him because it offers both an intellectual challenge and an opportunity to work primarily outdoors. 'Being stuck in an office really doesn't appeal to me', he says. 'That's why I decided against a career as a doctor. A lot of GPs won't like me saying this, but if they get anything interesting they normally have to refer it. The large-animal vet gets on with it and gets out and about.'

Trude does not share Mike's enthusiasm. She recognises that the experience she is gaining on farms is useful. And it will be essential if she takes a job in a mixed practice where vets are required to treat all sorts of animals from pets to livestock. However, there is an increasing trend to specialisation and, with that in mind, Trude has her sights set on a career in small-animal practice. She is certainly not enjoying herself today and complains that 'some days large-animal practice seems to consist of being cold, being kicked and being shitted on'.

However, Trude has proved in the past that she is no quitter. She has overcome enormous problems with the English language to get this far and is certainly not going to be defeated by a couple of routine procedures on a cow. There is something admirable about her approach in adversity, full of enthusiasm and good humour. 'Don't get your face too close' warns John Huxley as Trude approaches the cow to begin trimming its feet. Judging by the student's body language there is no danger of that. However, she soon relaxes and places a pair of clippers – which look rather like an outsize pair of pliers – on the cow's hoof. It is a surprisingly physical job and she makes several abortive attempts to clip the hoof.

Trude now has an audience urging her on with ironic cheers. Several of the farm workers have gathered round to watch her struggle. With hands thrust deep into their pockets and broad smiles on their faces they bellow 'Go on, get your back into it girl!' Their contribution is intended to be good-hearted, but it would be difficult to blame Trude if she regarded it as both intimidating and patronising. She is sweating, though still smiling, when she finally succeeds in exerting enough force on the clippers to trim the hoof. Pausing to look up at the men gathered round, she delivers her own verdict on her performance: 'I reckon I need to go to the gym more often'.

Now she takes a knife for some closer, precision work. Turning 180 degrees she leans into the cow's hindquarters and gently but firmly raises one of its feet. It is muddy and slippery and a little difficult to grasp, particularly when the animal attempts to shake its leg. But the cow is firmly tethered and Trude goes to work.

'You know about the problems of working in that position, don't you', warns John Huxley – and, right on cue, the cow opens its bowel and empties its bladder simultaneously. The back of Trude's blue overall is now brown and smelly. 'I knew that would happen' she says, managing a lame smile. Filthy and flustered, she is now unsure which part of the hoof she should be working on. The teacher is trying to direct her gently.

'There's one place where it's going to be overgrown' says John.

'The toe?' volunteers Trude.

'No.'

'The heel?'

'No. What are you going to have to take off?'

'The sole?'

'No.'

'Oh go on, help me. I bet it's really obvious.'

The fiery Dr Kieran O'Brien demonstrates a gentler side to his character.

John tries to help. 'Ok – big clue. It's a claw. Which one?'

'Ah ... it's going to be the medial claw.'

'No, it's going to be the lateral claw.'

'Oh, bloody hell', mutters Trude.

However, despite the difficulties the job is completed to the satisfaction of John Huxley and the onlooking farmer. He has been watching the young students with an air of amused detachment, but only because he knows the vet school will not short-change him on the service they provide. Allowing Trude Mostue and Mike Sandiford to have a go will certainly have slowed down the veterinary work, but the quality of that work will not be affected.

On the way back to Langford the students' talk is of their ambitions and the way the veterinary profession is changing. 'It's much more specialised than it was 30 or even 20 years ago', observes Mike, who reiterates that he is keen to work with large animals. 'At one time many vets were in mixed practice and they got to do a little of everything. But those James Herriot days are beginning to disappear I'm afraid.'

Trude is now even more convinced that she will concentrate on small animals. With John Huxley listening, she diplomatically stresses the value of her experiences on the farm but believes she already knows where her real strengths lie. 'I would like to think I am good with small animals and their owners. The people part is very important and I seem to be able to get along with pet owners. But someone will have to judge that later.'

First, though, she must be judged by her *bête noire*, Dr Kieran O'Brien. Each of the students must pass all the clerking rotations. Once the marks have been awarded Dr O'Brien will arrange a meeting with the student. 'I'm expecting a dramatic encounter', says Trude. 'Kieran is one of the reasons I've decided I don't want to specialise in large-animal practice.'

In his office Dr O'Brien contemplates the awkward meeting that lies ahead with some observations about his approach. He says that the quality of his teaching is directly related to the kind of student he is dealing with. By that he means their personality as much as their ability: 'If they are quiet and shy and don't ask too many questions I somehow seem to give them a lot less. Whereas if they are enthusiastic they get much more out of me.'

Before he meets the students O'Brien must have a debriefing with John Huxley, during which the two teachers will assess the performances of Mike Sandiford and Trude Mostue. They must decide whether the students have demonstrated an ability to translate their textbook knowledge into practical skills.

Getting a pass is crucial at this stage. Although the marks awarded to Trude and Mike won't count towards their final exams, a failure would require them to spend another week repeating their large-animal practice clerking rotation. With finals only five months way this would probably mean taking a week out of their Easter holidays. The holidays are already crammed with work anyway and they do not really have the time to take on any more.

When John arrives in O'Brien's office he is upbeat about the performance of at least one of his students. 'I think Mike Sandiford has done well this week. Foot trimming good, commitment good, practical skills above average and he knows some good stuff.' Dr O'Brien agrees. 'A good student, he will be a good vet and should pass his finals in

June.' The two men agree to give him 'a pat on the back' and an impressive mark of A/B.

They are not, however, impressed with Trude Mostue. O'Brien concedes that 'we've had worse students', but he is seriously considering failing her. He decides that he needs to refer the matter up and arranges a meeting with the Clinical Dean, Dr Frank Taylor. Dr Taylor is one of the most senior staff at the school and he will know how Trude is performing on her other clerking rotations. There is a suspicion that she is struggling in all areas.

Dr O'Brien summarises the problem to Dr Taylor in a typically forthright manner: 'She performed really badly on her large-animal practice'. The question they must both consider is a difficult one and has the added complication that the consequences of an unfavourable decision are potentially even more problematic. 'My concern', O'Brien tells the Clinical Dean, 'is that if we fail her and she's done equally badly everywhere else it might be totally counterproductive and she might just go to pieces.'

Frank Taylor shares those concerns and favours a more softly-softly approach. 'This is not a candidate where you go and say "for goodness' sake pull up your socks" – it would have totally the opposite effect. We don't want to play it heavy at all.'

Dr Taylor confirms that Trude has had problems on her other clerking rotations and that her performance has been 'patchy' throughout her four and a half years as a veterinary student. However, it is not all bad news. It is noted that in an important mid-year examination Trude achieved 66 per cent – a good mark.

Ultimately it is for Dr O'Brien to judge whether she has done enough to pass her clerking on large-animal practice. 'I'd be grateful, though, if you gave her a borderline pass', says the Clinical Dean. 'That way we could send out the message that this is a problem but not a disaster.'

O'Brien agrees but decides it is time for a face to face with Trude. Sitting in the empty canteen waiting to be summoned, Trude sips tea and predicts fireworks. 'He's got a problem with women. The only time he's ever thought I was useful was when he asked me to use my feminine charms to silence some noisy builders on the site. For God's sake!'

She is worried that he is going to fail her. 'I don't know how I could cope if that happened.' Trude's anxiety is based on her feeling that she is already working flat out just to keep up with the current work. 'A week lost repeating a clerking rotation would put me under incredible pressure', she says.

It is seven o'clock in the evening when Trude gets a message that Dr O'Brien is ready to see her. The veterinary school is now dark apart from a few lights in the large-animal practice block. This is where Trude is headed – a short walk of a few hundred yards, but enough to contemplate the awful prospect of failure. 'It would be a nightmare', she says.

However, a surprise is in store for her when she arrives. O'Brien is friendly, gentle even. More importantly for a student now filled with self-doubt, he is encouraging. The sting is immediately taken out of the meeting when he reveals that she has passed – albeit only just. Trude is obviously relieved, though she is well aware that she was a border-line case.

The Head of the Large-Animal Practice praises her commitment and notes a good exam result. 'You still think there's hope then?' Trude asks. 'Of course there's hope.' This from the man who, privately, still believes she will fail. However, he now appears to recognise that this student's best chance of confounding his prediction is to provide some encouragement along with the criticism.

The criticism is still apparent though. It has to be. Trude has an enormous amount of work to do if she is to get through her finals. O'Brien looks through her marks. Clinical side weak, academic knowledge weak, practical skills still a weak area. In particular, she needs plenty more practice on fertility examinations. 'It's really just a numbers game', he tells her. 'When you've done one hundred you'll be one hundred times better than when you've done just one. I suspect you haven't had as much practice as some of your colleagues.' Trude agrees and says she has already made arrangements to put her hand up more cows' backsides. Both the student and the teacher are relaxing now. All the fears of 'dramatic encounters' and 'fireworks' are receding fast. There is still tension in the air and an awkward formality that betrays their past difficulties, but this is developing into an unexpectedly positive meeting.

Dr O'Brien now feels comfortable enough to raise what he believes is one of Trude's main problems. He begins tentatively: 'We were unsure about your communication skills'. There is a short silence and Trude declines the implicit invitation to fill it. So he continues. 'Obviously, coming from a foreign country you're at a disadvantage ...'

This is the cue for Trude to open up. 'I must admit I do have a problem there. But it's a difficulty with language rather than communication.' In most situations, she says, she is fluent. O'Brien does not dispute that, noting that even her scientific vocabulary is on a par with the British students. However, Trude acknowledges that she has a real problem when she 'gets flustered'. When her confidence begins to evaporate, so does her fluency.

This meeting, though, may have begun the process of rebuilding Trude's confidence and healing the rift that has developed between her and O'Brien. As she gets up to leave she thanks him and both agree that it has been a useful meeting.

The beginning of a new chapter in their relationship perhaps? Well, not quite. Outside in the darkness of a now-deserted veterinary school Trude describes Kieran O'Brien as a 'Jekyll and Hyde character'. She is enormously relieved to have passed and genuinely pleased that they have had a positive conversation. However, she is also glad that this assessment marks the end of a stint on large-animal practice and, more particularly, the end of her contact with Kieran. 'It's odd when you've seen someone being very sarcastic and making you think that you're the most hopeless student in the world and then suddenly this person changes into a very nice person.'

Trude will now get the opportunity to move into an environment where she feels more comfortable. Her next clerking rotation is on the small-animal practice. No farms, no cows and, most importantly, no Kieran O'Brien.

Another student who is having difficulties with O'Brien is Julie Richards. Julie, an effervescent Liverpudlian who 'loves a laugh', is contemplating her week on large-animal practice in an uncharacteristically sober mood. She has already done a clerking week with him a few months back. The memories of her 'farm-animal hospital' assessment are not happy. 'I didn't get a very good report overall. I got a B, which was a pass, but Kieran's comments weren't very good. He wrote in my assessment that I was weak and immature.'

So, before this second clerking week with him has even begun, Julie is anxious. Since they last worked together she has also 'played' Dr O'Brien in the students' Christmas pantomime. 'I was selected for the part because I was the only one prepared to have a stab at his Irish accent. I hope he found it funny – or at least didn't find it insulting.'

Julie was so upset about being described as 'weak and immature' at the end of her last assessment that she went to O'Brien to complain. She acknowledges that he is a very good teacher, but she was concerned that he had made some wrong assumptions about her personality. 'I think he thought I was quite a giggly kind of girl and that I wasn't taking the week seriously. When I went to see him about it I said "Yeah, I do laugh a lot, but that doesn't mean I wasn't taking the week seriously". I am a laughing kind of person – I think that's a good way of communicating.'

Julie Richards' week on large-animal practice begins on a local farm. O'Brien has taken her there because a cow is calving. Modern farming practices – which involve mating different breeds – mean that cows often need help delivering their calves.

When they arrive the calf's head and forelegs have just poked their way out into daylight, but the rest of its body is still firmly wedged inside the mother. So Julie ties ropes to the calf's legs and, under O'Brien's supervision, tugs gently but firmly. It is an unusually straightforward delivery. Within a few seconds the calf plops on to the hay, blinking and coughing. He's fine, but O'Brien has a warning for his student. 'That was extremely easy, but don't expect many to be like that. Still, it was good practice, a nice easy start, and should give you a bit of confidence.'

Later in the week – in the dead of night and in bitter cold – Kieran O'Brien's prophetic words are vividly illustrated. Another Mendip farm and another calving, but that is where the similarity ends. This is one of those typically difficult births he was warning Julie about.

When the two of them arrive it is 20 minutes after O'Brien has received a call from the farmer. The cow has been trying to calf for two hours, but with little success. At this stage the calf isn't even visible. The cow is agitated and wary as O'Brien approaches her. He wants to tether her so that they can conduct an internal examination. Once she is tethered, Julie is given the job of putting her arm inside to try to establish the problem.

'Is the calf moving?', asks O'Brien.

'Yeah, I think so; it's quite big', says Julie.

'Ok, what's the next step?'

'Attach some ropes to the forelegs?'

'Yep, that's right. So away you go.'

The task isn't as simple as last time, though. First Julie has to grope around trying to find the calf's legs. She can feel that the cow is straining, attempting to contribute to the delivery, but now she really needs some help. Julie is straining too, pulling all kinds of faces as she attempts to attach the ropes to the calf's legs – which are now visible, but only just. Once she has completed that task the real physical work begins. Julie and her teacher are joined by the farmer, and the three of them lean back with their full weight and heave.

It is a noisy business, with the animal mooing and the humans grunting from their exertions. Soon Julie, O'Brien and the farmer are sweating and panting as well, their breath clearly visible in the air. The bitter cold is temporarily forgotten. After several minutes of tugging the calf is dragged on to the hay. A still breathless Julie is delighted, and now the struggle is for the right adjective. 'It's wonderful, great, really fantastic!' O'Brien is pleased too. Although he has done this hundreds of times before, it is satisfying work, emotionally and physically. 'The calf will be fine. He's raised his head within a few minutes of delivery, which is a good sign. He should be standing within an hour.'

The following morning Kieran O'Brien and Julie Richards find themselves confronted with an animal which is having real difficulty standing. This time, though, they are dealing with a horse. The bitter cold weather is persisting, accompanied now by a strong wind. Julie is freezing and tired, but the examination must be conducted outside the stables. As the owner leads the horse towards Kieran and Julie it is clear that this is an animal in considerable pain. She is trying to raise one of her back feet off the ground.

'Oh, you are very sore, aren't you, you poor thing', says O'Brien soothingly. Less soothing to Julie's cold, red ears are his next words, directed this time at the owner. 'What I'm going to do now is to leave you with Julie, who's a final-year student, and she'll have a look at it.' With that he marches off briskly across the stable yard.

Julie is wearing plenty of clothes and her characteristic smile, but these do not offer much protection from the elements or a potentially cantankerous horse. She approaches with extreme caution and gingerly grapples with the problem leg, which the animal is in no mood to allow her to take hold of. 'I'm trying to test the hoof to see if there is a localised area of pain,' she tells the equally anxious and cold owner, 'but it's so painful I can't get anywhere near it.'

After several minutes she is ready to accept defeat. She can't handle this horse – literally – and she wants help. Where's Kieran? He is standing fifty yards away, arms folded, out of earshot but looking on intently. No sign yet of him stepping in to offer advice.

'Did you ride her yesterday?' Julie asks the owner.

'No.'

'Did you notice a cut on her yesterday?'

'No.'

'Is she eating?'

'Yes.'

At last O'Brien approaches, sensing perhaps that his pupil has gone as far as she can with the initial consultation.

'Ok, have you come to a diagnosis?'

'The whole leg is swollen', Julie offers in response. But he persists. 'Have you seen anything else?'

'No.'

'Have you checked carefully?'

'Not carefully, no. It was difficult. The horse is in a lot of pain and really is not keen on me touching her.'

'Just run your fingers up against her hair', advises O'Brien. 'Gently, very carefully. And watch your stance. Don't crouch, bend.'

Under her teacher's guidance and prompting Julie is making progress. She has detected a small cut. 'So, what do you think?' he asks. 'I think', says the student, 'that it's very likely that an infection has got into a little wound and travelled up the leg.'

'Ok, good', he says. 'Has she got a temperature?'

'I haven't taken her temperature. Would you like me to?'

'Yes please.'

The brief and polite exchange about the horse's temperature doesn't hide O'Brien's irritation or Julie's realisation that the task is routine and should have been performed without prompting. She sprints off to the Land Rover to collect the thermometer.

Anxious to make amends she is back within a minute. The thermometer must go in the horse's backside. She approaches cautiously.

'Now that's a very good way to get kicked', says O'Brien.

'Is it. Why?' asks Julie.

'You're approaching from the right-hand side. You should always work on the left-hand side. That's the side most horses are used to us working on.'

A minute later Julie is able to confirm the temperature is normal.

'Does that rule out infection?' asks O'Brien.

'No' is Julie's response.

'No, certainly not', he says emphatically, determined to reinforce the point. He moves towards the horse and, with the confidence and knowledge only experience can bring, takes a firm hold of the horse's leg. Julie had struggled for several minutes in a vain attempt to exercise such a grip. O'Brien knows why. 'This leg is exquisitely painful. You've only got to touch it anywhere to recognise that.'

The diagnosis may be over, but the lesson isn't. Kieran O'Brien continues to fire questions at Julie.

'What are we going to do?'

'Antibiotics?'

'Yes. How?'

'She's pretty sore so we should try and give it by injection.'

'Initially yes. What else should we do?'

'I don't know.'

'This horse also needs anti-inflammatory painkillers because she needs to be walked four times a day.'

'Ok', says Julie, withering a little under the sustained barrage of questioning. And it isn't over yet.

'Prognosis. Riding next week?' asks O'Brien.

'No, not next week.'

'Right. Did we ought to see her again?'

'Yes.'

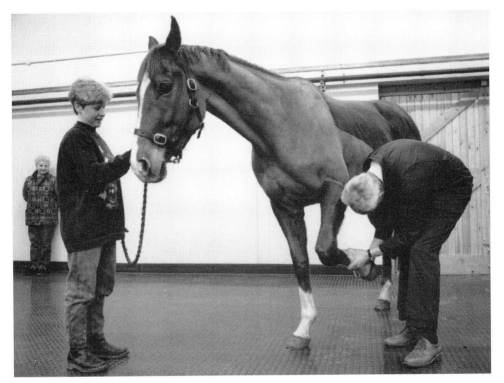

Vet Alistair Barr working on the left-hand side of his patient.

At last Kieran O'Brien appears to be satisfied. Julie gives the horse its injections and O'Brien assures the owner that 'within 48 hours the horse should be a lot less lame'. The diagnosis, the prognosis, the treatment and the lesson are complete.

Julie Richards has learnt a lot and confesses to a growing respect for the sometimes fiery doctor. 'He really is an excellent teacher. He knows his stuff and is never boring. I think I've got on really well with him. It's been a very good week. But I still don't know how he will assess me. My horse examination wasn't very good, but I thought I was pretty good on the cattle.'

Dr O'Brien will consider Julie's assessment with houseman John Huxley. Seated behind his desk thumbing through the student's file, he refreshes his memory about their last encounter.

'She was with us previously on hospital rotation and we gave her quite a bad report, actually. I've written down here that she was rather weak and immature. I actually thought it was quite an improvement this week.'

'Absolutely, I agree. She was very good', says John Huxley.

Kieran notes that there was a marked improvement in what he calls her 'attitude': 'She was much more serious. She's still lovely and bubbly and friendly, but her approach to her work appears to be more appropriate.'

'She's a pleasure to work with', agrees John.

Having laid to rest any lingering doubts about Julie's personality and attitude, the two teachers begin to award marks for her assessment. On this they are much tougher.

'Practical skills. What do you think?' Kieran asks John.

'Pretty good. She's either a B or an A/B.'

'B I think', says Kieran. 'Ok, now what about clinical skills?'

'Average', says John.

'Yes, I had her on a horse examination today, and it wasn't very good. So, overall, I think her clinical skills are very average. She'll have to improve.'

Dr O'Brien also sees room for improvement in her academic knowledge and her communications skills. 'Julie is a very chatty girl, but a lot of what she has to say is rather superficial and not very enquiring.' This may be a harsh judgement, but he sets high standards. He has to because in six months time Julie and her colleagues will be out there on their own, and that is a real responsibility for those who teach them. 'We're the last hurdle they jump before they're let loose on the general public, and no one should expect it to be easy', he observes.

Seen in that context, Julie Richards has done rather well. The Head of the Large-Animal Practice acknowledges as much when he awards the overall mark. She will get a B, which is an average pass, but her assessment will also contain a note recording a significant improvement on her last clerking week with large animals.

John Huxley comments that she is 'very good with clients'. O'Brien endorses that view – and goes even further. 'I think she'll make a very good vet actually. She'll certainly pass her finals. I don't have any doubts on that score.'

Small animals

THE BRITISH love their pets. In fact, it appears that we love them more and more year on year. The growth in pet ownership is now so phenomenal that there are real concerns the country may soon face a shortage of vets.

The Bristol Veterinary School doesn't just train the 'pet vets' of the future, it is also a major national centre to which veterinary surgeons refer small-animal clinical cases. A new £800,000 hospital bears testimony both to the increasing popularity of pets (or 'companion animals', as the profession prefers to call them) and to a recent 40 per cent increase in the school's student numbers.

The hospital's consulting and diagnostic block is really the 'front of house' part of the school – the bit that most of the public get to see when they bring their pets for specialist care. It is a fine advertisement. Friendly, efficient, light, airy and impossibly clean .... 'Should I leave my dog outside?' jokes one owner arriving for surgery this morning.

The block includes waiting and reception facilities, consulting rooms and a series of specialist treatment rooms equipped for the diagnosis and treatment of cases in the fields of dermatology, orthopaedics, cardiology, urology and ophthalmology. Bristol has internationally recognised experts in all these areas.

The hospital also includes the latest kennelling and intensive-care facilities, which are considered essential for a veterinary teaching school that now accepts cases from all over the United Kingdom. Many of the dogs and cats brought to Langford have complex disorders that require intensive investigation and treatment.

Enormous advances are continually being made in the development of diagnostic techniques and methods of treatment. This means that animals that might previously have been put to sleep as undiagnosed, hopeless or inoperable cases are now being presented to specialists at the school in the expectation that they can be saved.

A vital part of the care of those animals are the kennels and intensive-care facilities, which, in addition, are widely used in the practical tuition of student veterinary surgeons. Badly traumatised animals, severe acute medical cases and dogs and cats that have undergone complicated surgery frequently require 24-hour intensive care. The previous facilities were only capable of holding nine dogs and eight cats. The upgraded unit is equipped to deal with 50 animals.

The new small-animal hospital also includes a feline centre. Cats are among the nation's most popular companion animals. The number of people owning them has risen dramatically – from four million in the 1960s to over seven million in the 1990s.

Mirroring this increase in the cat population, feline medicine has become one of the most rapidly developing areas of veterinary science. The Bristol Veterinary School has been at the forefront of this development and is now the major feline clinical centre, not just in Britain but in the whole of Europe.

Over the last ten years Langford has built up a team of specialist clinicians dedicated to maintaining the health and welfare of cats and to the diagnosis and treatment of their disorders. A major charity, the Feline Advisory Bureau, has established a Lectureship in Feline Studies at Bristol.

Against this background it is not surprising that the feline centre is a large part of the new small-animal hospital, recognising the importance of adopting an individual approach to cats as a separate species. There are three consulting rooms, offices, a treatment area, a separate waiting-room and a lecture theatre for teaching purposes. The centre is the cat's equivalent of Great Ormond Street Hospital for Children.

For the students, then, it is a privileged environment to begin their training, surrounded by the best modern facilities and some of Europe's most highly regarded specialists. But as well as referrals, the school offers routine health care for pets.

It's now February and, having scraped through her large-animal practice, Trude Mostue is about to confront the equally awkward challenges posed by small animals. She is looking forward to it. Her personable, sunny nature equips her with the charm and confidence to deal with the most important relationship – that between the vet and the animal's owner. A good 'bedside manner' with the patient is a useful start, but, as they don't talk or pay the bills, students have to learn to direct that bedside manner towards the customer.

It is noon and the vet-school clock tower is chiming 'All things bright and beautiful', as it does every quarter of an hour. 'Drives me mad', remarks Trude. She is not alone. It drives everyone mad. Indeed, many years ago some students attempted to silence it. However, their efforts at sabotage succeeded only in removing a few chimes and, by common consent, the effect of 'All things bright and beautiful' minus several chords was even more irritating.

Right now, though, the chiming is a welcome reminder that lunchtime is approaching and, with luck, Trude can look forward to a rare break. The clerking system and breaks rarely dovetail, but small-animal practice is considered one of the easier clerking rotations. It is also Trude's favourite veterinary practice, the field that she plans to pursue if she qualifies.

Before lunch Trude has to deal with a routine consultation – two cats and one owner. Before the consultation she is relaxed. She chats happily about her fondness for both companion animals and their companions. It was this combination that first attracted her to the veterinary profession. She likes animals, of course, but 'I like people even more and this is a great job for getting to meet lots of people. The way you cope with clients really has a big impact on how you are going to do with the animals.'

The client, Stephanie Noble, is a regular. As well as bringing her cats to Langford for routine check-ups, she has also used the school's more specialist skills and facilities. Her St Bernard dog had an operation to have a ligament replaced. 'The staff here are all excellent. Always very good and attentive – friendly too. I trust them and, no, I don't mind the students. They've got to learn somewhere.'

Mrs Noble is relaxed as she introduces the cats to a receptionist in the waiting room. Both of them are peering out of their wicker carriers. There is a very active black kitten called Calais that needs vaccinating but for now seems determined to escape. 'Great fun and very

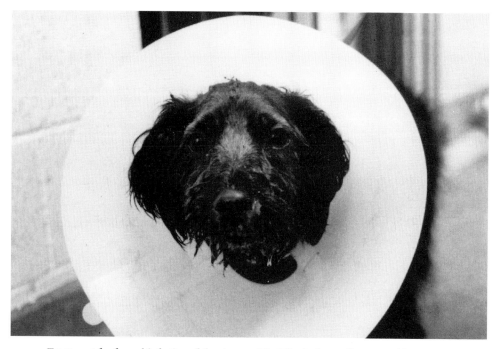

Treatment for fungal infection of the sinuses. The Elizabethan collar stops this mongrel pulling out the tubes to his nose.

noisy', says Mrs Noble, '... never stops meowing. Now the other one is a bit more of a problem.' She gestures in the direction of a plump ginger tom called Winnie, lying motionless in his basket. The tom is looking on with a somewhat fierce expression but is suspiciously quiet.

Before the owner can explain the symptoms, Trude breezes out of the consulting room. 'Hi, how are you. Can I help you with the basket?' The 'bedside manner' is off to a promising start. Mrs Noble hasn't met Trude before but warms to her immediately. 'Yes please, that's kind. But please handle the basket gently. Winnie is a little nervous. Always has been ever since we collected him from an RSPCA rescue centre.'

In the consulting room, gleaming new and equipped with the most modern facilities, Trude will be supervised by Dr Alison Blaxter. Alison is the head vet in the small-animal practice and Trude's personal tutor. All pupils are assigned personal tutors for the duration of the course, someone they can turn to for help with any non-academic problems.

Modern facilities and round-the-clock care mean this cat in the intensive-care unit has a greater chance of recovery.

Right now, though, Trude is expected to fend for herself. Alison leaves the consulting room, and her student is now alone with the client. This is deliberate, a chance for Trude to take some responsibility. It is her job now to carry out a routine examination and then present the specialist with a diagnosis.

'Who shall we do first?' asks Trude brightly. 'How about the little one?' Mrs Noble releases the catch on the basket and gently lifts a very lively black kitten on to the examination table. 'This is Calais.'

'She's sweet. How old is she?'

'She's nine weeks. And she meows a lot. Quiet cats are not for me.'

'So I can hear', laughs Trude.

'She likes to crawl up on to people's shoulders. It's her favourite place.'

'So I can see', says Trude as Calais leaps at her and crawls her way up to that favourite place.

After Trude has managed to prise a determined and increasingly

Student Julie Richards injecting Tolly, a diabetic cat.

noisy little kitten off her shoulder she establishes that the animal needs two routine vaccinations. To administer them, the student needs a teacher in attendance. Dr Blaxter is called.

It is at this point that the problems begin. Alison is keen for Trude to prepare and administer the vaccinations herself, albeit under supervision. However, the preparation gets off to a shaky start – literally. Trude is clearly nervous and her hands aren't as steady as she'd like them to be. She manages to stab the syringe into the vaccine bottle but can't draw the fluid.

'Leave it', says Alison gently, and then with a smile she offers Trude a syringe with the correct dosage. 'Here's one I prepared earlier. You go over and give Calais her first injection while I prepare the second one.'

Trude's confidence has taken a minor knock. You can see it on her face. But the bedside manner is still working well. 'Mrs Noble, if you could just bring your kitten here I will give her the first vaccination. Very straightforward and very quick.'

The noisy Calais is brought back to the table, where she is eyed by the ominously quiet Winnie. 'Ok, this is it,' says Trude cheerily, 'don't worry, little thing. All over in an instant.' With that she grips the kitten firmly and pushes the needle into the scruff of the animal's neck. And out the other side. 'Oh my god,' cries Trude, 'it's gone straight through!' She's right. It has. Injecting through the scruff is a common but embarrassing mistake – one that students make hundreds of times every year.

It is at times like this that veterinary theory counts for little. Trude has read all the textbooks. She knows what she has to do. It's just that right now dexterity is more important than an academic appreciation of the procedure. Handling a live, squirming and increasingly unco-operative kitten is not as easy as it might appear.

This, of course, is what the fifth year is all about, the whole purpose of the clerking rotations. They are designed to put the students into awkward situations, to give them the kind of hands-on experience they will need when they become practising vets in a few months' time. Right now, though, Trude would rather pursue a hands-off approach.

'Will you do it?' Trude implores her teacher. But Alison can see that the owner is smiling and relaxed and that Calais is none the worse for her experience. No need to step in yet then. This is not a real crisis – only a crisis of confidence for a red-faced Norwegian student who can do little to hide her embarrassment, given the vivid contrast with her very blonde hair.

'Don't worry about it', says Alison reassuringly. 'Try and hold her by the scruff when you're injecting her. That way she can't wriggle and your aim should be true.' A little nervous laughter from Trude and she is ready for a second shot. 'Ok, let's see if we can do this right now. Don't worry Calais. I think I've got it.' But she hasn't. Once more the vaccine trickles down the side of the kitten's neck. 'Oh no, I've done it again. I'm so sorry', says Trude, talking first to Calais and then turning to her owner. 'I've never done that before.' But Mrs Noble is still smiling and Alison remains patient and encouraging. 'Don't worry about it. It's just nerves. It's very embarrassing, but we all do it.' However, this particular learning experience is at an end. Calais has had enough and Alison administers the injections in seconds with experienced dexterity.

The clock chimes one o'clock. 'All things bright and beautiful.' Behind the wicker bars of his basket Winnie the large Tom looks neither bright nor beautiful. 'Actually Winnie is just rather highly strung. A cat of a nervous disposition. But very affectionate', says Stephanie Noble. Trude is looking of an increasingly nervous disposition herself, particularly as Alison disappears from the consulting room leaving instructions that the student should make the initial diagnosis.

As Winnie is removed from his basket there is no hiding the fact that this is an animal that finds a visit to the small-animal practice extremely stressful. At least Trude can claim some empathy. The cat is agitated but still oddly quiet. 'Tell me about Winnie', begins Trude, sounding for all the world as if this is a conversation she would rather not have. Mrs Noble explains. 'Well, he's about five years old and very neurotic. At one point we were thinking of putting him on to valium because he was so stressed. But he's been a lot happier recently. Until, that was, he lost his meow.'

'Pardon me?' inquires Trude, her incredulity overcoming her nerves.

'He's lost his meow.'

'Oh dear. When did he stop meowing?'

'About a week ago.'

An uncomfortable silence descends on the room as a mute cat, a concerned owner and a bemused veterinary student stare at each other across the examination table. Trude throws a desperate glance towards the door through which Alison vanished only a few minutes ago. It obviously seems like hours and, for the first time, Trude's bedside manner is beginning to fail her. What does she do or say next?

'Has she got any diarrhoea?'

'Well, I wouldn't know, dear. He's a fully grown cat and I don't tend to follow him when he goes to the toilet.'

'Of course not', blushes Trude.

'I wonder if it's got something to do with the kitten', inquires the ever-patient Mrs Noble.

'What do you mean?'

'Well, Winnie hates Calais. Perhaps the stress has struck him dumb.'

'I think I'd better take his temperature', says Trude, momentarily recovering her composure.

'He doesn't like having a thermometer stuck up his bottom,' warns Mrs Noble, 'although Alison seemed to manage it last time.'

At last. An excuse to summon help. 'I'll just go and get Alison then' says Trude, moving swiftly to the door, which, in her mind, must be marked 'Escape'.

Alison reappears with Trude hovering at her shoulder. Clearly this is where the student intends to stay – one step behind. The qualified vet takes control. She begins an examination of the cat's mouth and throat, all the while talking to him in reassuring tones. 'Just relax. Take it easy. Don't worry. I know you don't like coming here any more than I like going to the dentist.'

Alison swiftly decides that a thermometer up the backside of a

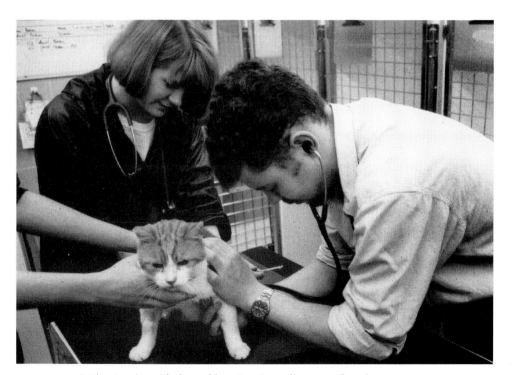

Getting to grips with the problem. Jon Coupe listens out for a heart murmur.

nervous cat is probably not the smartest move. So what's the diagnosis? Nothing more complicated than a sore throat. Cause unknown, but probably treatable with a simple anti-inflammatory injection.

'Injection?' sighs Trude. 'Oh no.'

'I think I'll do it,' says Alison, 'if that's ok with you.'

'Absolutely ok with me.'

'Poor old puss,' whispers Alison as she administers the injection, 'life is pretty hard for a nervous cat without a meow.'

For the last hour and a half it hasn't been a barrel of laughs for Trude Mostue either. She's still apologising to Calais, Mrs Noble and Winnie as they leave. The apologies are obviously appreciated, but they are neither sought nor needed. The only creature who has really suffered during the last 90 minutes is Trude herself. The huge sigh of relief as the consulting room door closes is testimony to that.

Alone in the room with Alison, Trude's attempt at yet another apology is interrupted by her teacher. 'Don't worry. Everyone's missed with an injection. I certainly have. You just need some more practice on live animals.' 'I'll try it on my boyfriend', laughs Trude.

It's two o'clock. 'All things bright and beautiful ....' Lunch is off the menu again for Trude today. Afternoon surgery begins immediately.

Exactly six hours later the chimes echo round a now largely deserted vet school. This time they signal not a lost lunch break but the beginning of a long night for one of Trude's fellow students. Twenty-two-year-old Pat Ridge is about to face a real emergency. During the course of the next ten hours he will get an unscheduled lesson in birth, surgery and death.

Pat is the student representative, the main point of liaison between the staff and the pupils. He is a local boy. His father runs a deer farm just a few miles from Langford in the village of Backwell. At the beginning of the fifth year he had a reputation among some of the staff for being a bit of an awkward character and a student who might struggle to make the grade. But in the last few months he has settled down and impressed even Kieran O'Brien, who had been rather critical of him.

Pat Ridge has been clerking on the small-animal practice since breakfast time. It has been a routine day. He is preparing to go home when Fina pads into the surgery.

Fina is a three-year-old German Shepherd. Her owner, Sue Elliot, is worried. Fina is due to produce a litter of pups and has been 'nesting' for 16 hours with no visible sign of progress. The dog is clearly agitated. She cannot keep still, turning round and round in circles, lying down for a moment and then getting up again almost immediately. Fina is also whining continually, scratching at the green-tiled floor and tugging and pawing at a blanket which the Elliots have allowed her to bring. This nesting behaviour is perfectly normal. What is abnormal is the length of time she's been doing it.

'I've been up with her since 4.30 this morning and she's given up pushing', says the anxious owner. 'All she's doing now is panting and whining.'

The vet in charge is Sarah Caney. She asks Pat Ridge to carry out a routine external examination. Pat approaches Fina cautiously, but he has no need to worry. Despite her agitation and preoccupation the dog is friendly and stoic. The student handles her gently and Fina even manages a brief wag of her tail.

'I'm worried', Sarah Caney confides to her student. 'This is Fina's third litter and the previous two were just normal deliveries. I'm concerned that a puppy could be stuck in the birth canal.'

Sarah tells Mrs Elliot that she'll need to do an internal examination. Pat stands aside as Sarah puts on her gloves and searches for a blockage. Fina appears to accept the probing without complaint, but her owner looks tense as she cradles the dog's head in her lap. No one speaks, and the rather oppressive silence in the surgery is punctuated only by Fina's whimpering.

Sarah senses the tension and attempts to engage the owner in conversation. 'Do you breed from all your bitches?' 'No, just Fina.' It is a short reply with a long full stop. Mrs Elliot is too tense to engage in small talk. After a while Sarah announces: 'She feels quite relaxed but I can't feel a puppy. I can't say for sure whether there's a blockage.' As soon as the examination is complete Fina resumes nesting, eventually dragging her blanket under the surgery examination table. When the dog has settled some of the tension in the surgery is relieved.

Mrs Elliot wants to talk now. She is worried that she may have misread the signs. 'I was just thinking that I may have acted a bit quick.'

'No, I don't think so', says Sarah reassuringly, relieved no doubt

This page: (Top)
Student Rachel Privett with
Heidi, a Golden Retriever.
(Bottom) From left, students
Trude Mostue, Sam Robinson,
and Mark Johnson comfort
Heidi while Mike Sandiford
takes a blood sample. Heidi
has been admitted with
defective legs.

Facing page: (Top left)
Mike Sandiford X-rays Heidi,
who is now diagnosed as
having liver cancer.
(Top right) Heidi, near
the end.
(Bottom) Sam and Rachel
engaged in a vain attempt to
save Heidi, who is put to sleep
a week later.

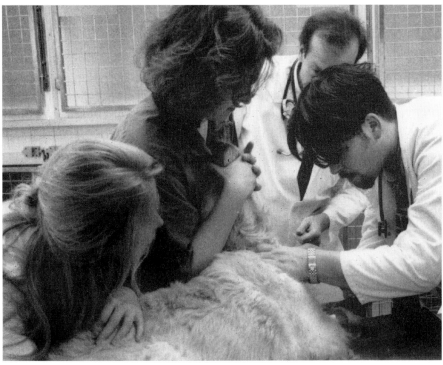

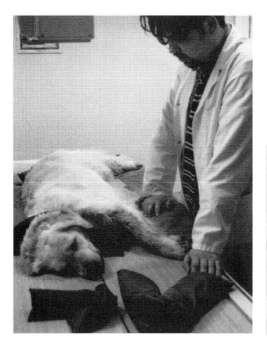

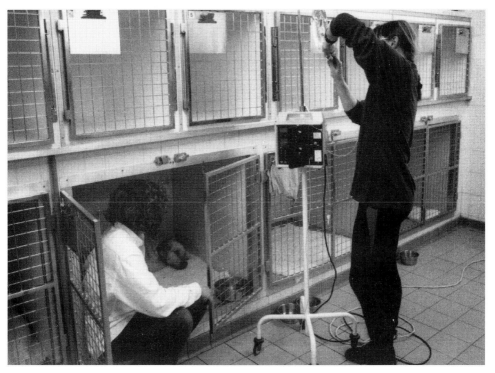

that dialogue has been re-established. 'I feel pretty sure she's ready.'

'We have been breeding for 16 years and have had countless litters. This has never happened before', says the owner.

Sarah is happy to acknowledge Sue Elliot's experience and, indeed, expertise. It reinforces her view that something is wrong. 'I'm sure your interpretation of her behaviour is right. The good thing at this stage is that Fina is relatively happy and stable, so we're acting at the right time. The wrong thing now would be to leave things because there would be a high risk of dead puppies – and a risk to Mum too.'

Sarah turns to Pat Ridge, who has been looking and listening intently but has said nothing for half an hour. She tells him that the puppies may have to be delivered by caesarean section. This is exciting news for a student hungry for experience but potentially bad news for the remarkably good-natured German Shepherd. Surgery carries its own risks for Fina and her pups, and Sarah is anxious to avoid it if at all possible. By now the dog has reappeared from under the table and has resumed her restless scratching of the floor and circling of the room. Pat is instructed to give her a dose of oxytocin, a hormone that should induce labour within 20 minutes. As the injection is administered Mrs Elliot winces. Still no complaints from Fina though.

Dog and owner are then left alone while vet and student retire to another room to weigh up the options if the injection doesn't work.

'Perhaps she's not ready', suggests Pat.

'No, we know she's ready, that's really not the issue', replies Sarah. 'The question is, why isn't she moving into the second stage and pushing for herself. Perhaps the oxytocin will do the trick.'

It doesn't. Half an hour later Pat and Sarah sit down in the consulting room with Mrs Elliot to talk about where they go from here. Fina will need an X-ray and some blood tests to try to establish the location of the pups and the condition of their Mum. Pat clips the fur from one of her legs and inserts the needle to draw the blood. Fina lets out a sharp yelp of pain – startling Pat, who pauses, clearly expecting some sort of retaliation. It never happens and the test is completed without further fuss. Fina is a remarkably good-natured dog, as she will demonstrate time after time over the many long hours which lie ahead.

Pat takes the blood sample to a machine that measures blood-glucose levels. The reading is instant and reassuring. No real cause for concern at this stage. So there is an opportunity for Sarah to test whether Pat understands the implications of what is going on. When they are on their clerking rotations the students are rarely permitted the luxury of simply standing and watching. If they are not 'doing', their teachers will be asking questions and expecting rapid, accurate answers.

'What problem will we face if she has a low glucose level?' asks Sarah.

'Well, several things', replies Pat, uncertainty infecting his voice.

'What things?'

Pat blushes. 'Several things which I can't quite think of right now.'

Sarah coaxes an answer from him. 'Come on, you know.'

'Lethargy?'

The answer is posed in the form of a question, betraying both uncertainty and a lack of confidence that is often evident in students at this stage. As it happens, Pat is right. The concern now is that after 18 hours Fina might become too exhausted to push her pups out. If she begins to run low on energy, she may need an intravenous drip of glucose and saline to help her get through what lies ahead.

First, though, she needs an X-ray. It might help Sarah and Pat to establish how many pups there are, whether they are still alive and why they are reluctant to make an entry into the world. Because Fina is pregnant they cannot sedate her, so she is lifted on to the operation table and pinned down with weighted bags. Now, for the first time, she is really frightened and begins to shake uncontrollably.

Pat tries to reassure her. 'Good girl. Alright sweetie. There's a good girl. Don't worry. Don't panic.' In a moment he must dash behind a screen while the X-ray picture is taken. He knows it could be difficult. 'The worry is that during those few seconds Fina will summon what little strength she has left, throw the bags off and leg it. Then we don't have a photo but do have a problem.'

To prepare the distressed dog for the X-ray, the machine is passed over her several times while Pat and Sarah are still in the room. They are worried that the noise will frighten her into bolting, and this way – accompanied by words of encouragement from the vets – she at least has the chance to become used to it.

Fina is calming down now, apparently resigned to whatever indignities must be heaped on her to help her give birth. Pat and Sarah sense an opportunity and disappear, hoping that the dog will stay put. She does, the X-ray is taken, and five minutes later they are studying the images and trying to make head or tail of them.

At first the images are confusing. There seem to be spines, legs and heads everywhere. Sarah explains that it is hard to tell one pup from another and the only way to make a reliable guess about numbers is to attempt to count the number of heads. 'However, it's a bit of a jumble in there', she concedes. 'It looks like there are quite a lot of puppies.'

Sarah tells Pat she thinks there are eight or nine. She can see the head of one in particular, a big puppy that seems to have its head engaged in the birth canal. It's difficult to tell whether it's stuck, but it might be. An ultrasound examination confirms that some of the puppies are still alive. How many is anyone's guess, but there is hope.

By now it is 10.30 p.m. and two and a half hours since Fina arrived at the surgery. The prospect of a caesarean is increasing by the minute. Sarah must balance the risks of the operation against the risks of waiting and hoping. The longer Fina is left, the more tired she will become and the greater the threat to the lives of the puppies.

To add to the pressure, Mrs Elliot has some understandable reservations about a caesarean. She reasons it will be distressing for Fina. There is also the risk that she could die under anaesthetic and, even if that fear proves groundless, the operation may mean she will not be able to have any more litters. Mrs Elliot wants to continue breeding from Fina.

However, Sarah thinks it is at least time to alert the surgeons to the possibility of a 'caesar'. While she telephones the surgical team, Pat rushes to call his housemate and fellow student, Fiona Green. It is her evening off, but he knows that she is very keen to see some emergency surgery in the small-animal practice. Such enthusiasm and commitment are commonplace. All of the students willingly give up what little spare time they have if there is a new opportunity to learn, a chance to experience something they haven't witnessed before.

Within a few minutes Fiona has joined Pat and makes a half-hearted attempt to portray herself as the reluctant student. 'I'm here', she tells Sarah, 'because Pat dragged me out of the bath to see a caesar.' She certainly hasn't been dragged, but she may have arrived with rather premature expectations. There is still no guarantee of a caesarean. For at this moment there's a shout from another room where Mrs Elliot has been watching Fina. She's just given birth to her first pup. At 1 lb 4 oz it's unusually big and is already on the teat, displaying a healthy appetite to become even bigger. Sarah calls him 'Mr Fatso'. He was probably the cause of his mother's problems.

The caesarean is put off and between 11 p.m. and 1 a.m. Fina has three more pups, one of which is dead. The surviving pups appear to be doing well. They are making little contented snuffling noises and suckling with relish. 'Very, very cute', says Pat.

Then everything stops again. It's 1.30 in the morning and the students go outside so that Pat can have a cigarette. It is pouring with rain – but they seem oblivious to it, caught up in the excitement of a real-life emergency.

'I've never seen a normal whelping, let alone a caesar', enthuses Fiona. 'Making a decision about when to take an animal to surgery is definitely one of those things that can be a bit frightening. It's fascinating though, too, watching someone else going through the decision-making process.'

However, for all the fascination it is undoubtedly a relief to the students that, at this stage, the responsibility does not rest on their young and inexperienced shoulders. The day when it does may not be far away, though – and that is why Pat and Fiona are the keenest of observers, knowing that in a few months they may well be qualified vets, making the decisions themselves.

Inside the surgery Fina still hasn't delivered any more pups and Mrs Elliot is becoming increasingly anxious. But, outside, Fiona and Pat make no attempt to disguise their curiosity.

Like Fiona, Pat Ridge has reached his fifth year as a veterinary student without ever seeing a caesarean on a dog. Horses, cows, sheep, yes. But never a dog. 'It's just the same as a cow – isn't it?' he asks Fiona. She laughs, and he realises it will be very different. Cows stand up for caesareans.

Fiona and Pat are now both hoping that Fina won't be able to give birth to the rest of her pups naturally so that their curiosity will be satisfied. 'I'd like to see her rushed down to the surgery before any more puppies arrive', jokes Pat. 'And if they do fall out on the way down there, I will personally stuff them back in!'

Both students laugh, recover their composure and go back inside. The vet in charge is still reluctant to go for a caesarean. They want to wait a little longer. Fiona doesn't. She can't stop yawning and neither can she forget that she has to be up at quarter to eight to begin her equine clerking rotation. She does not have to be here and, just before 2 a.m., overcome with fatigue, she finally calls it a night. Her calculation is that she may be waiting for an operation which will never happen. 'I'm going to bed because it doesn't look like Fina is going for surgery. But I bet the minute I leave they'll decide on a caesar.'

Well, not quite a minute. Forty-five to be precise. At 2.45 a.m. Sarah approaches Mrs Elliot with some advice the owner doesn't really want to hear. The vet has decided that they have held on long enough in the hope that Fina will produce the remaining pups naturally. It is time to prepare for a caesarean. She is worried that Fina is becoming exhausted. 'If she wasn't so tired it wouldn't be so worrying. And if she had just one more puppy it wouldn't be so worrying either. But we know there are at least another three in there. What do you think?'

'I think I must take your advice', says Mrs Elliot, gazing down at Fina. 'You really are exhausted, aren't you poor girl. Is there any point in me staying?'

'No, not really. We'll call you.'

With that Mrs Elliot gets up, pats Fina on the head, whispers, 'You'll be all right girl, don't worry' and heads off home.

Once the decision has been made the atmosphere changes immediately and dramatically. From being a sleepy place, the surgery suddenly livens up. The theatre lights go on. The surgeons scrub up. Pat does too. This is a privilege. If students are told to scrub up they know they'll get to see some action – maybe even to help.

Pat Ridge has now been up and working for 19 hours. He is operating on adrenaline but desperately wants to see it through. And not just for the sake of curiosity and experience. 'I want to leave here knowing Fina is ok, and hopefully most of her puppies too.'

Fina is shaved and given an anaesthetic. The operation lasts for an hour and a quarter. Four pups, each a little larger than a human hand, are delivered. All emerge looking limp and lifeless and all but one eventually respond to treatment. To stimulate their breathing they

The survivors. Fina's puppies, delivered by caesarian, making good progress back home.

are rubbed vigorously on the back of the neck and given a drug called Dopram.

When it is all over, seven live pups are put in an incubator in the intensive-care unit. Fina is taken to the kennels to sleep it off and Pat is given a mop and bucket to clean up the floor. He has now been on the go for nearly 24 hours. Unshaven, dog-tired and contemplating a morning of lectures he is, nevertheless, elated. 'It was great. You don't often get the chance to watch life-and-death decisions being made. After tonight I reckon I'll be a little better equipped to deal with it when I have to face those decisions myself.'

Two hours later he is back at his desk, attempting to stifle yawns. Fina is conscious and looking remarkably bright-eyed and bushy-tailed. At lunchtime a grateful Mrs Elliot collects her German Shepherd. She may not be able to breed from her again – but at least Fina has survived, along with seven of her pups.

A couple of days later comes the distressing news that two tiny female puppies died soon after arriving home. From an initial litter of ten puppies, then, just five have survived, all of them male. Bearing in mind the complications, though, it could have been much worse. Pat Ridge certainly considers it five lives saved rather than five lost. It is also a priceless piece of hands-on experience for a young veterinary

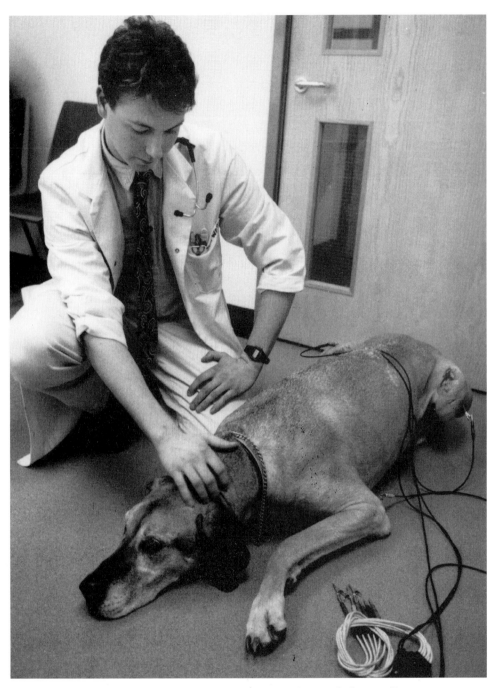

Student Jonathan Wray with a Great Dane wired up ready for a cardiogram.

student – 'something', he says, 'that no textbook can prepare or equip you for'.

The whole experience has clearly been a particularly rewarding one for Pat. But it was also gruelling. Perhaps it will help prepare him for what promises to be a particularly demanding career. However, it does not altogether explain the attraction of a career that involves long, antisocial hours and so much stress that suicide rates among vets are now some of the highest in the country.

With exams only four months away, all 66 final-year students are totally consumed by the demands of the course. Now, as well as having to revise, they are on 24-hour standby for emergency cases on their clerking rotations.

So why do they do it? Is it simply that they can do it, that they are clever enough? Not according to the Head of the Veterinary School at Langford. Professor Philip Duffus believes that, despite the demands, a career as a vet is still perceived as something romantic. It is a notion which, for a generation at least, appears to have been inspired almost single-handedly by an author.

'James Herriot has been hugely influential for many of these kids and it's pointless to deny it. Of course they wouldn't get in if they came to the interview and said, "I've read lots of James Herriot books and it looks like a fun career". But if you question them closely, often that's what started them off.'

But the James Herriot factor isn't only reflected in the number of bright young children who have been encouraged to follow in his foot-steps. It is also a reflection of the oft-quoted phrase that we are a 'nation of animal lovers'. Millions of people helped propel Herriot to the top of the best-selling lists – and they weren't all aspiring vets.

Professor Duffus believes that this is one of the reasons why vets are regarded with both esteem and affection. 'It still amazes me, the British public's link with animals. The need for us to be associated with animals goes back an awfully long way. The demand for our services says a huge amount about how much people in this country care for their animals.'

Frank Fletcher is one of those people. It is 9 p.m. and he has just driven into the vet school with Rosie. Rosie is his much-loved Siamese cat and she is critically ill. Frank has been referred to Langford by his vet and has made a difficult 40-mile journey from Wiltshire in heavy snow.

Sarah Caney, the small-animal practice vet, is waiting. She has called out student Pippa Hughes to help. The phone rings. It is Frank Fletcher on his mobile phone. He has arrived but can't find his way to the small-animal hospital. Hardly surprising as it can be difficult to find your way around Langford's sprawling collection of buildings even in the daytime.

Pippa and Sarah go out into the snow to look for Rosie's owner. They find him within a couple of minutes, anxiously clutching his cat carrier, and hurry him into the warmth of the small-animal hospital.

Frank Fletcher loves his cats. He has six, including Rosie, and implores the vets to do whatever they can to save her life. He knows she is seriously ill; his own vet has told him that much. 'Most of the fight has gone out of her', he says. 'She's normally a bundle of energy and very talkative.'

Sarah asks Pippa to give the cat a thorough check-over, warning her that once out of the carrier Rosie might be difficult to restrain. She need not have worried. Rosie is listless and in danger of slipping into a coma.

While the student tends to the cat, the vet talks to the owner. She wants to know as much as possible about the cat's history. Where did he buy her? What does he feed her? Is she free to go outside? Do they live in the country or in town? And what are the symptoms?

The problem had started three days previously when Rosie suddenly became very lethargic. 'Her coat went dull within hours. She was fine, and now she looks like she's nearly dead', says Mr Fletcher. He thinks Rosie might have been poisoned. 'She's a good mouser and I reckon she could have picked up some poison from a nearby farm.'

Sarah is not convinced and is pretty sure that what she is dealing with is a diabetic cat. The owner is puzzled – he assumed it was only a human condition. Sarah tells him it is not uncommon in cats. In fact there are two diabetic cats in the small-animal hospital at the moment.

Rosie is in real danger and Mr Fletcher now knows it, his distress clear as he constantly strokes and whispers to his cat. Sarah gently spells out the prognosis. 'Things are out of control at the moment and the condition is definitely life-threatening. The next 24 hours will be critical and I wouldn't like to offer you any guarantees.'

What she can offer the distressed Mr Fletcher is the reassurance that Rosie will receive round-the-clock care at one of Europe's best small-animal hospitals. 'I'm very happy to accept her and do whatever we can', she says. 'We'll keep our fingers crossed, but even if we pull her through the acute stages, it may take a while to stabilise her condition.'

Frank Fletcher nods, signs a consent form, kisses his cat and makes to leave. Before he does, though, he has a question. How much is the treatment likely to cost? Judging from his distraught state, it is difficult to imagine any price being too high. 'I think at the moment a cost of two to three hundred pounds is going to be approximately right, depending on what we do', says Sarah.

As soon as Mr Fletcher has left Sarah and Pippa begin to develop a plan of action. Pippa identifies the cat as being dehydrated and hypothermic. They run a series of blood and urine tests. Rosie's blood is particularly thick because of the dehydration and Pippa finds it difficult to extract a sample. Sarah has to step in to carry out the test.

The results of the tests are not encouraging. Rosie has a host of problems. The most immediate threat to her life is that her blood is dangerously acidic. But she is also dehydrated, hypothermic and jaundiced – and she has high glucose levels.

To deal with the dehydration they put her on a drip, 'administered', Sarah tells Pippa, 'as rapidly as we dare'. Rosie, who appears to have little life left in her, is placed on a heated mat and wrapped in a blanket for the hypothermia. She is given insulin for the high glucose levels. They'll try to deal with the acidic blood by administering bicarbonate of soda.

It is now 11 p.m., two hours since the cat was admitted. Sarah knows that if Rosie is to stand any chance of surviving she will need care throughout the night with regular hourly checks. This is a job for the students, and Pippa is given the task of ringing round her colleagues and organising a night rota. It will involve two of them every hour – one to hold the cat, the other to administer any treatment which is required. Steve Leonard is supposed to be working with dogs, but he too is called for the 3.30 a.m. slot to help Pippa.

Meanwhile Sarah Caney rings the owner. It is late, but he answers on the first ring. He has been too anxious to go to bed. Sarah's manner in these situations is a model for any young vet student: calm, caring, gentle and as reassuring as she can be. She runs through the test results, concluding that 'the blood acidity is my main concern. Uncorrected, Rosie will certainly die during the night. We'll do what we can, but you must understand that she's still critical. A very ill cat.'

An exhausted Sarah leaves for home and bed. Throughout the night a succession of bleary-eyed students wander into the small-animal hospital in pairs. They are on their own, though Sarah is on the end of a telephone if required. Rosie is getting the kind of intensive care that probably would not be economically viable were it not being carried out by students hungry for experience. In hard-cash terms the bill might run into thousands rather than hundreds of pounds.

Fortunately for Rosie and her doting owner, the school does not operate on strictly commercial lines. During such emergencies its 'contract' with the public is mutually advantageous. Mr Fletcher gets five-star treatment for his cat at a bargain-basement rate, and tomorrow's vets get an opportunity to accumulate that most priceless asset – experience.

A great deal of effort is lavished on Rosie the diabetic cat. There is still no guarantee that the intensive care will pay off but, against the odds, she makes it through the night. She is not yet out of danger – but in the morning, refreshed after a night's sleep, Sarah Caney sounds a note of cautious optimism. She pays tribute to the efforts of the students and the staying power of their patient. 'I think it's a tremendous achievement for her to have got this far. I think she's going to make it.'

Over the next few days Rosie continues to make good progress. The alarming lethargy that was so evident when she was close to death disappears and the distinctive 'chatty' Siamese meow returns. She begins to eat and drink on her own and, by the time Mr Fletcher and his wife Pam arrive to collect her a week after she was admitted, the only problem that remains is the diabetes. That is manageable as long as they have the patience and the money. A diabetic cat cannot survive unless its owner has plenty of both. Many people confronted with the realities of the condition decide reluctantly that they must have the animal put to sleep. It is still conceivable that the Fletchers might chose this course. Conceivable, but unlikely.

Pam Fletcher loves the cat every bit as much as her husband does. They are sitting in reception in the small-animal hospital flicking

An uneasy time in ICU.

through an array of cat magazines and reflecting on their seven days without Rosie. 'She's never been away from home before', says Mrs Fletcher. 'She might be sulking.' That comment alone effectively brings to an end any speculation about Rosie's future. Her adoring owners may not know what lies ahead, but it is patently obvious that they will do whatever it takes to keep her alive.

Mr Fletcher says it's been a very emotional time for them. 'I won't cry when we're reunited though,' he smiles, 'I'm too tough.' Mrs Fletcher predicts that she 'will probably burst into tears.' She is right. As soon as Sarah Caney emerges from a consulting room with Rosie, the cat starts meowing and Mrs Fletcher begins to cry. No one in the reception area bats an eyelid. There is a strong sense that this kind of emotional reunion between companion animal and companion is fairly commonplace.

This, though, is not the end of the story. Sarah is trying to make herself heard over the joyful sobs and meows to deliver some very important and possibly unpalatable information. She tells the Fletchers that Rosie will need an insulin injection every day for the rest of her life. They take it in their stride. Will they have to do it themselves? Yes. What does it involve? 'Follow me', says Sarah, leading them away from reception and down a corridor to a consulting room. It is time for their first and only lesson on how to treat a diabetic cat.

Rosie is placed on the operating table for a demonstration. Sarah explains that a cat's diabetes is like human diabetes. Her blood-sugar levels are too high. The glucose is coming out in Rosie's urine, leaving her short of energy. 'That's why the poor old girl has become so thin', says Sarah. 'Her condition has forced her body to use its fat reserves. The insulin will help her body use the glucose.'

The explanation is simple enough, but it is becoming clear that teaching the owners to inject their cat is going to be rather more complicated. The Fletchers are certainly willing, but are they able? They look worried, and there is a debate about who should do the injecting. It is agreed that it will be Mrs Fletcher. She does not look delighted at the prospect but swallows hard and asks a touchingly naive question. 'Will I have to scrub up before I do this every time?' 'No,' laughs Sarah, 'that's a bit over the top. Just observe general good standards of hygiene.'

The vet shows them how it is done. Rosie lets out a sharp meow – a reaction, according to Sarah, not to the pain of the needle but the surprise of the cold fluid flowing under her skin. 'It doesn't hurt. I'm sure you'll mind much more than Rosie.' It is a prediction that the Fletchers would be unlikely to dispute at this moment. It must be running through their minds that this tricky procedure is going to be necessary every day and that neither Rosie nor Pam is going to enjoy it.

Mrs Fletcher is handed the insulin bottle and the syringe. It is important that she gets the dosage right, but initially she cannot draw any fluid at all. 'Even this bit is really difficult,' she groans, 'and I haven't even started yet.' Her husband steps in with helping hands and, although it takes several minutes, between them they manage to prepare the injection. Now Mrs Fletcher is on her own again. She approaches Rosie gingerly, brandishing the syringe rather like a sword. The cat is facing away from her and is being held down by Sarah. However, just before the needle goes in she manages to turn her head and look at her owner. The eye contact seems to throw Mrs Fletcher, who pauses, syringe poised in mid-air. Can she go through with it? After a big sigh and a moment's contemplation she delivers the first of what will be thousands of injections accompanied by a loud meow. From now on this will be part of their daily routine. The Fletchers decide they will do it first thing every morning, just before Rosie's breakfast.

The lesson is now over. 'You see, it's not that difficult', says the vet encouragingly. 'No, I suppose not', responds Mrs Fletcher doubtfully. But whatever reservations she has about her ability to care for a diabetic cat, they are forgotten as she turns her attention to the staff who have saved Rosie's life. 'You've done a marvellous job', she tells the vets as she and her husband are about to leave, clutching a box of syringes, a bottle of insulin and a very lucky cat. At the reception desk, though, they are in for a rude shock.

'Just the bill now, I'm afraid', says the receptionist. 'That'll be five hundred and thirty-two pounds and thirty-eight pence please.'

Frank Fletcher smiles weakly and reaches for his cheque book. He says nothing, but his expression is enough.

'Weren't you warned how much it was going to be?' asks the receptionist.

'Yeah – two to three hundred pounds.'

Everyone suddenly looks very embarrassed. But, in a particularly timely entry, Sarah arrives, acutely aware that her quote for the treatment had been about half what is now being asked. A rapid and whispered consultation with the receptionist and the bill is reduced. It turns out that Sarah's original estimate was based on the assumption that Rosie was unlikely to survive.

However, the awkward moment over fees is a minor hiccup. The Fletchers are both smiling as they carefully place the cat carrier containing Rosie on the back seat of their car. Was it worth all that money? 'Of course,' says Mr Fletcher, 'it's a life, and if you value it you don't mind paying. With cats you either like them or you don't. And we do.'

Mrs Fletcher agrees. 'Rosie is a living being and you've just got to do your best for her. And us? Well, we're just silly cat owners I suppose.'

Cats are also the focus of discussion in a nearby office at the Small-Animal Practice. Trude Mostue is coming to the end of her clerking week there and Alison Blaxter, the vet in charge, is preparing an assessment of the student's performance. Predictably, Trude's handling of Calais, the kitten who needed vaccinating, and Winnie, the cat in search of his lost meow, will feature prominently in the discussions.

Trude is due to see Alison later to discover whether she has done enough to convince her teachers that she is worthy of a pass. First, though, Alison must produce an assessment, together with one of her assistants, Eithne Comerford.

This is a crucial assessment for Trude. She scraped through on her large-animal practice, but only after Dr Kieran O'Brien had expressed a number of reservations about her performance. All the clerking weeks are important, but, for Trude, small-animal practice is particularly important because it is the area in which she wishes to specialise.

The mood is upbeat as Alison begins her meeting with Eithne. 'We've got a very positive comment from a client about Trude, which was very nice. She took the trouble to send a letter praising Trude.' It turns out that the letter is from none other than the owner of Calais and Winnie. Despite the student's abortive attempts to vaccinate one and restore the meow of the other, she still managed to impress Mrs Noble. Alison reads the note to Eithne: 'Trude was very good and I recommend her. She was friendly and seemed very confident. I would be happy for our cats to see her again.'

This is a good start, and both teachers agree that one of Trude Mostue's biggest assets is her likeability. 'I find her enthusiastic, helpful and interested. She's also very friendly and chatty', says Alison Blaxter. Eithne agrees, adding that Trude's academic knowledge is pretty sound.

However, that is effectively the end of the good news. Noting the student's 'pretty poor injection technique', Alison expresses concern about Trude's practical skills in general. Eithne is worried too. 'She seems to lack confidence and she can be rather haphazard in her approach to cases.'

If it all sounds rather damning, that is not the intention. The clerking weeks, and the subsequent assessments, are designed not only to test the students' skills but to improve them as well. Any criticisms are used to focus renewed efforts on shortcomings which need special attention. The emphasis is very much on helping the student through any difficulties rather than making premature judgements. In particular, all the staff involved in assessments are keen to identify why a student might be struggling.

With Trude the why is predictable and understandable. Alison is convinced that most of it is down to language problems. Everyone at the school recognises the enormous difficulties that Trude has had to overcome, dealing with a very demanding course in an unfamiliar language. Most of the time she appears to be remarkably fluent but, as Alison observes, when she is put under pressure all that can change. 'With the clients it can be very difficult when she becomes flustered. I think she still thinks in Norwegian a lot of the time and she obviously has problems with some of the colloquial English phrases we use.'

By the time the 20-minute meeting between Alison Blaxter and Eithne Comerford concludes it is clear that Trude Mostue could be facing the prospect of repeating the small-animal practice clerking week. Alison is certainly thinking of failing her as she thanks Eithne for her input and awaits Trude's arrival.

Dr Blaxter's assessment technique is a highly effective combination

Taking a urine sample isn't always easy. Trude and Rachel lend a helping hand.

of carrot and stick. Like all the teachers at the Bristol Veterinary School, she is aware that Trude's fragile confidence needs building up and that her language problems require a measure of understanding rather than an overdose of criticism. So, when Trude sits down nervously in her office, Alison is all smiles and informality. The message she has to deliver will not be a welcome one but, before giving the bad news, she opens with some encouragement. 'We were very impressed with your enthusiasm and your interest. You were very helpful in all aspects of your rotation. We've given you an excellent grade for enthusiasm.'

The relief spreads across Trude's face and she appears to relax a little. Perhaps this is not going to be so bad after all. Alison also produces Mrs Noble's letter. Unsolicited praise from clients, she says, is praise indeed. The student is obviously delighted and encouraged, although she is open and honest enough to remember the problems she had vaccinating the kitten. 'That was so embarrassing', she winces. 'To inject through the scruff not once but twice ... oh dear.' 'Yes, your injection technique certainly requires some further practice', laughs Alison. 'It is rather an important feature of being a vet that you can do it smoothly and without distress to the animal. But we've all made the same mistake and I'm sure it's something you can sort out.'

Recalling the incident seems to draw the sting out of what could have been a very difficult meeting. Both women are now relaxed, and the assessment moves seamlessly from carrot to stick.

'You seem to lack confidence in practical tasks', remarks Alison. Trude readily agrees. 'I know, it's true. I've heard that many times before. I think that I'm still getting used to expressing myself in English.'

'Are you still thinking in Norwegian?'

'I'm not sure actually. I think it's a mixture.'

Alison suggests that Trude might benefit from concentrating more on scientific explanations and less on the colloquial. 'You know your scientific terms; don't make things more difficult for yourself by trying to translate it all into everyday English.'

At this point the teacher reminds the student that she can dispute any observation that she does not believe to be true. 'It's all true and very fair', remarks Trude with typical candour.

'Ok, good. Well, I'm also worried about your approach to cases', says Alison. 'I've been listening to you with clients through the hatch in my office.'

'Oh, no!' exclaims Trude. 'I didn't know you could do that.'

But Alison Blaxter has been doing that, and to good effect. On several occasions when Trude believed she was alone with a client Alison had been eavesdropping, analysing her strengths and weaknesses. This is continuous assessment with an added dimension.

'What I heard concerned me. In all honesty you have a tendency to approach your cases in a haphazard fashion. You haven't got a structure.'

'I know what you mean. I must be better organised sometimes.'

'Well, you must be more methodical certainly. The basis of being a good vet is being methodical. A lot of what we do is very routine.'

By now Trude knows where all this is leading. She has failed her clerking week on small-animal practice – though when Alison delivers the verdict it is couched in much more positive terms. 'We've all really enjoyed working with you and overall I very much think that you would benefit from repeating this week.'

Trude is disappointed, but she receives the news in the same positive manner in which it was delivered. 'I feel I would benefit from doing it again as well. I'm not surprised by anything you said. I really think you picked up on all the right things.'

Trude is now going to have to find an extra week in an already hectic schedule. The repetition is essential, but that will not make it any easier as finals approach. She will probably need to schedule it into her Easter holidays – the veterinary students' last real uninterrupted opportunity to revise prior to exams in June.

In the meantime, Alison Blaxter explains, she must submit the assessment she has just made. That means that Trude has a failure on her file that must be overturned before she can sit her finals. She knows that the file remains open, and that her failure can be revoked and replaced with a new assessment – but only if her second crack at the small-animal practice clerking rotation is rather more successful than the first. It is a challenge which she believes she will be equal to, but one nonetheless she could have done without. The pressure on Trude Mostue can only increase over the coming months.

Horses

Hᴏʀsᴇs ᴀʀᴇ big business at Bristol. The Langford site has some of the country's leading specialists and now possesses an equine diagnostic centre that reflects their expertise. The new £600,000 building is also a reflection of the clinical income the veterinary school is earning from horses. The Equine Centre, the new small-animal hospital and a research centre have been built over the last five years and they are all self-financing. The Equine Centre itself covers five acres and provides the most up-to-date and extensive facilities for diagnosing and treating disorders as well as improving horse welfare. It contains specialist facilities for the clinical investigation of respiratory, orthopaedic and cardiac conditions.

As well as dealing with clinical problems, the new centre helps racehorses and other 'equine athletes' by assessing fitness using a wide variety of advanced technologies, such as high-speed treadmills. The treadmill is not dissimilar to the kind of running machines found in most gyms. Horses can gallop at speed on it, enabling Bristol's specialists to evaluate heart and lung function and diagnose lameness. Early diagnosis and treatment of injury greatly improve a horse's chances of returning to competition.

It is Saturday morning and Fiona Green is nearing the end of her equine clerking rotation, which began on Monday. It has been a long and important week for a student who is beginning to think she might specialise in horses when, and if, she qualifies. Fiona has spent most of the time completing a daily round of assisting on horse operations and diagnosing problems. It has all been fairly routine stuff, although at Friday lunchtime she had to deliver a detailed presentation on one of her cases to eight of her tutors. These presentations are assessed, along with the student's performance during the rest of the week, and the marks go towards the final degree.

The weekends are supposed to provide an opportunity for some time off. However, the clerking rotations do not officially end until Monday morning. This means that students have to complete regular four-hourly checks and be on call for emergencies on Saturday and Sunday.

Any hopes Fiona may have had for a relatively easy end to a gruelling week are quickly dispelled when she arrives at Langford at 8 a.m. on Saturday to do her first check. The equine specialists have been up since dawn on a full-scale colic emergency – one of the most serious cases this year. Fiona will be expected to help.

Colic is a stomach disorder that is particularly dangerous in horses. It has a number of different causes and, unless the reason for the condition is quickly established and appropriate treatment given, the animal can easily die. It is usually a job for a surgeon because the cause or the extent of the problem can only be known with certainty by opening up the animal's stomach. This is a major operation, so the decision is a critical one.

The horse, called Jasper Carrot, is owned by David and Liz Gabriel. They live on the edge of Dartmoor and left home at 4 a.m. this morning for the two-hour drive to Langford. David Gabriel is a vet and an equine specialist himself. However, although he believed he had the expertise to deal with the condition, he recognised that his own practice did not have facilities that matched the particularly impressive ones at the veterinary school. David knows Langford well, having graduated from the school in 1973.

As Fiona arrives he is talking anxiously to the equine vet at Langford, Jane Craig. He and his wife are clearly tired and emotional. Indeed, Liz Gabriel is close to tears and will remain that way for several hours to come. Jasper is a much-loved horse. The Gabriels have owned him for 15 of his 23 years and Liz, who rides him twice a day, considers him to be more of a pet than a working horse. 'Some people have horses and buy and sell them like cars', she says. 'For me, though, they're much more like a cat or a dog – one of the family. Lots of horse owners aren't as sentimental as me, I suppose.'

'I felt if I'd left him any longer we were going to be looking at a situation where I just couldn't move him', says David Gabriel, explaining his dramatic decision to drive to Langford in the early hours of the morning. Jane Craig agrees it was the right move. 'It's obviously good to get him here so quickly. That will give him his best chance.'

At his age Jasper is particularly susceptible to colic and, in his present condition, his chances of survival are no better than fifty/fifty. Jane gets the Gabriels to sign a surgery-consent form. 'The only thing I have to do now', she says, ' is to ask you that if we find something that we cannot treat do we have your permission to put him to sleep on the operating table to save him further pain and distress?' The Gabriels nod their consent.

For Fiona there is just time for a quick cup of coffee before Jasper is given pre-medication injections and prepared for anaesthesia. Fiona will be assisting in the operation, her first colic. It is an exciting and rather nerve-racking time for her. For David Gabriel there are mixed emotions. Worry that Jasper won't pull through, mixed with a real feeling of nostalgia and *déjà vu*. 'It's all very familiar territory for me. It's very strange being back here and not being really involved. I just have to stand back, let everyone get on with it and hope for the best.' In fact, although David will stand back, it will be from a privileged vantage point as he has been given permission to go into the operating theatre to watch. Liz Gabriel climbs into their four-wheel-drive vehicle with the empty horsebox attached and prepares for a long wait on her own. She is convinced that she has ridden Jasper for the last time. 'He's been a good friend, but I don't think I'll ever see him again.'

While surgeon Dr Geoff Lane prepares the operating theatre, Jane Craig, assisted by Fiona and five other students, is organising the premed in an adjacent room. The walls and floor are covered in bright red padded plastic to protect horses from injury when they become groggy from the anaesthetic and go down. Once Jasper is unconscious he has to be pulled to the centre of the padded room. There, straps are attached to his feet and he is winched on to a trolley, which is then wheeled into theatre. Next, using another winch, he is lifted a few feet and gently rolled on to the operating table. At this stage a horse is an incongruous sight, flat on its back with its legs in the air. This is the position Jasper will remain in throughout the operation.

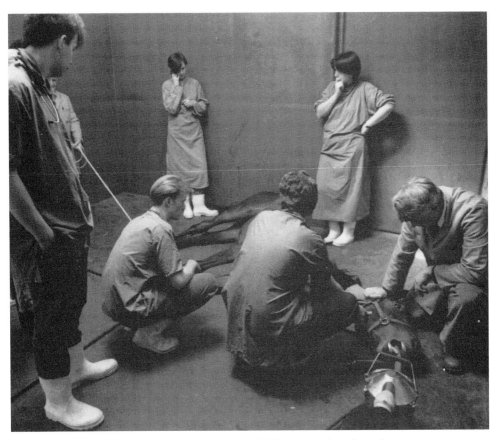

Anaesthetising a horse. A group of fifth-year students learn how.

Meanwhile, David Gabriel is having a quick word with Geoff Lane and talking, this time, not so much about Jasper's problems as his own. David is having difficulties recruiting an extra vet for his expanding practice. There is a shortage of vets in the industry. 'I'm looking for a young British graduate at the moment, but so far my adverts haven't attracted much of a response. It's a real problem.' One potential young graduate is preoccupied with more immediate concerns. Fiona knows that Jasper may die on the operating table. 'Until we've opened him up, though, we won't know how serious it is', she says.

For the next two hours or so Fiona will stand just a couple of feet away from the surgeon, who is now opening Jasper up. When Geoff Lane first reaches into the horse's abdominal cavity there are no obvious signs of the problem. It is a bloody and physically demanding operation that involves pulling yards of intestine from the horse's body and working through it by hand trying to find the cause of the extreme pain the animal has been suffering. With Fiona gazing on intently, Geoff announces that he can find nothing wrong.

'Perhaps', he says, 'it's a bowel problem.' He decides to open part of the bowel up and push the contents into a bucket. Fiona helps. It is a procedure that creates a risk of infection but which often offers more clues to what is wrong.

Not this time though. The faeces are normal, so Dr Lane returns to the intestine. After more than an hour he eventually locates the problem, a benign growth of fatty tissue called a 'lipoma'. It looks rather like a child's swingball or, as Geoff describes it: 'In appearance it's pretty similar to the traditional South American weapon called the bolas'. As the horse moves around the lipoma gradually wraps itself around the gut until it is strangling the animal's insides. It is not difficult to imagine why it is excruciatingly painful for the horse. In fact, Jasper has two lipomas wrapped around his intestines. Both are successfully removed.

This is an enormous relief to all the surgical staff as well as to a particularly interested observer. Until now David Gabriel has been standing well away at the back of the theatre. But now he steps forward to look at the lipomas, which, laid out on the floor, are both a couple of feet in length. A crisis seems to have passed and David is happy to talk about his feelings over the last few traumatic hours. 'I was more than a bit upset. I see a lot of colics because our practice specialises in equine. But however objective you try to be, when it's your own animal you're inevitably going to become more emotional.'

Fiona Green's emotions are all about excitement. 'It was really good … just fascinating. You hear all about the anatomy in lectures and it all sounds like a bit of a jumble. But when you actually get to see it, it all begins to make sense and somehow doesn't look so complicated.'

With that, David Gabriel leaves the theatre to give his wife the encouraging news. It is still not certain that Jasper will make a full recovery, but he will now have the benefit of Langford's outstanding aftercare facilities and things are certainly looking up. Liz, who is still sitting in the car, manages an anxious smile as David opens the door and leans in to update her. 'What's the prognosis?' she asks. 'The prognosis is good', he replies. 'Jasper is a tough bird. I'm just glad we brought him here. It totally vindicates our decision to drive him to Langford.'

The relief overcomes Liz, who now allows the tears which she has held back for so long to flow. 'I just feel so happy because when I said cheerio to him an hour and a half ago I thought I'd never see him again. He means so much to me – like a child really, I suppose. But when it happened I felt so helpless, even though I am married to a vet. You can't reassure a horse like you would a child.'

Jasper has now come round after his anaesthetic. He is back on his feet and the Gabriels leave the car together to go and see him. Fiona is there too and, while Liz chats to Jasper, David, sensing an opportunity, begins a conversation with the student. He knows that she is interested in working in a mixed practice that specialises in equine. 'That's what we do', he tells her. 'We have got some quite good new facilities courtesy of the BBC!'

It turns out that David Gabriel's practice is acting as advisor for the successful BBC TV drama series *The Vet*. The students know all about the series. On the rare occasions when they have time to watch television they like nothing better than to settle down as a group of informed critics and scrutinise an episode for factual inaccuracies. David concedes it is not 'always true to life', but he points out that it is 'drama, not documentary, and as such the series has some merit'.

However, the vet and the student are not here to argue about the merits of television drama. Rather bizarrely, Fiona finds herself undergoing her first job interview in a stable just a few yards from where the interviewer's horse is recovering from a major colic operation. She takes it in her stride, asking as many questions as she is asked. It is all very informal, although David appears to be selling his practice rather harder than the student seems to be selling herself.

Undoubtedly this is a reflection of the rather extraordinary state of the veterinary jobs market. The unscheduled interview is a graphic illustration of just how much in demand Fiona and her fellow graduates will be in a few months' time. They are clearly not destined for the same fate as many other university graduates, who often face long periods of unemployment after their finals. Tomorrow's vets are already in demand today and most of them will be in a strong position to pick and choose.

David Gabriel well remembers his own time at Bristol and knows that even though the students are likely to find it easy to secure a job this is, nonetheless, a daunting time in their lives. 'You're in awe of the people who are teaching you and what you're just about to be expected to do. And all the time you're wondering whether you'll be able to do it. The acid test doesn't come until you actually qualify and are let loose on the public. Only then do you know if you are any good.'

The impromptu interview concludes with David asking Fiona to come down to Devon for the day to look at the practice. She says she would like that, and they agree to fix a date once Jasper has recovered. The horse has to remain at Langford for a few more days. It is Langford's aftercare facilities that had been a critical factor in the Gabriels' decision to bring him to the veterinary school. Over the next fortnight the wisdom of the decision will be reinforced when Jasper suffers another setback which, once more, leaves him fighting for his life.

For now, however, the Gabriels leave for home believing that the worst is behind them. Fiona can relax a little too, knowing that her equine rotation is over and that a job offer may be just round the corner. But no one could have predicted what was just round the corner for Jasper. Four days after the colic emergency his condition begins to deteriorate rapidly.

The horse suddenly develops extreme diarrhoea, refuses to eat or drink and is soon dehydrating fast. Pippa Hughes and Toby Gemmill, final-year students now on the equine rotation, are assigned to do regular checks. Jasper is put into an isolation unit and connected to a drip. On Wednesday he is so ill that Pippa and Toby stay up all night simply watching him. Every time they go into the stable they have to ensure that their boots and gloves are sterilised. Throughout the week they take it in turns to sit in the doorway of the stable watching over the very sick horse and encouraging him to drink.

Samples are sent off to the laboratories, but already Bristol's specialists and David Gabriel are fairly sure of the diagnosis. About ten per cent of horses carry the salmonella virus, which can be activated by any kind of violent shock to the system. And a complicated colic operation is certainly a shock to the system. Drugs can help, but with Jasper already in an extremely weak state it is looking increasingly unlikely that he can pull through. At this stage the vets are giving him only a 30 per cent chance of survival.

By now the students' equine clerking rotation has changed again and Steve Leonard – not a great lover of horses – is assigned to Jasper full time. This means that throughout his clerking week Steve is unable to work on any other cases because of the risk of infection. Nevertheless a close, if initially uneasy, relationship develops between the two of them.

Then Jasper begins to show encouraging signs of a remarkable recovery. His appetite returns and Steve is detailed to regular grass-cutting duties. Twice a day he takes a bucket and a pair of shears into one of the meadows around the veterinary school and prepares a feast to whet the appetite of the most discerning herbivore. Steve looks for a particular kind of grass: 'It mustn't be too lush because that acts as a laxative – which, for a horse with diarrhoea, is not great.'

So, is Jasper thankful for all this care and attention? Well, not exactly, according to Steve. It is certainly true that the horse's physical condition is improving by the day. But as he grows stronger Jasper is also becoming more cantankerous. 'He can be a bit of a git', says Steve bluntly. 'When I first met him he bit one of my colleagues. We're getting on a little better now, and he's a bit friendlier. Having said that, though, when his owner came round he bit him too!'

A fortnight after he was first admitted for colic Jasper is ready to go home. He will still have to be isolated because salmonella can be passed on for up to four months. The horse will need regular testing, and only when he has been clear of the virus for five consecutive days will he be allowed out again.

Steve Leonard knows that he has witnessed and contributed to an extraordinary turnaround in the horse's condition. And, being Steve, he has a personal theory about why Jasper recovered. He believes it is all to do with the horse's less than endearing personality. 'I am very surprised that he has recovered. Earlier in the week I didn't think he would live. I reckon he survived because he is a very stubborn, cantankerous old git. I'm certain that's what got him through. He's still managing to have a few swipes at me now and again!'

The Gabriels arrive to collect Jasper. The bill comes to £2000 – 'excellent value for money', according to David Gabriel. However, it is still a lot of money and a prime example of the need for horse owners to take out insurance. 'If they don't,' says David, 'some of them could find themselves in big trouble. It often means that we vets can't do a comprehensive job on a sick animal. We have to trim around the edges in order to cut costs.' It is fortunate that David can afford to pay out of his own pocket because, as he rather sheepishly admits, he is not insured himself. However, the reason is understandable. 'I didn't think it was worth it because I had always anticipated being able to do any treatment myself.'

Liz Gabriel, meanwhile, is leading Jasper into his trailer box in preparation for the trip back to Devon. When the horse is with her there is no sign of the bad temper that has accompanied his recovery. Once he is in the box the two of them share a carrot – his mouth on one end, hers on the other. Liz is clearly overjoyed at getting him back. 'It's been a long fortnight, but they've all been fantastic at Langford. I was just pleased he was in the best place possible, and you have to put your trust in the people who are looking after him – the veterinary students as well as the qualified vets.'

She is exhausted, emotionally and physically drained. Throughout Jasper's lengthy stay at Langford Liz has insisted on travelling up from Devon almost every day. She is now looking forward to being able to ride him again. But that won't be for a while because, even after he gets home, Jasper will be in quarantine for some time.

A few days later Fiona Green makes the hundred-mile journey to Devon, arriving on a snow-covered Dartmoor for her interview. David Gabriel shows her round one of his small but well-equipped surgeries. He tells her that they have recently spent a great deal of money on diagnostic equipment, although he stresses that any worthwhile diagnosis has to be backed up by solid experience. 'It's relatively easy to make a diagnosis. It's also usually relatively easy to treat a condition. But what people really want to know is the prognosis – how are things going to turn out. And you only really get that through experience.'

Fiona notices the old-fashioned paper filing system. 'You're not tempted to get computerised?' she asks. David says he is thinking

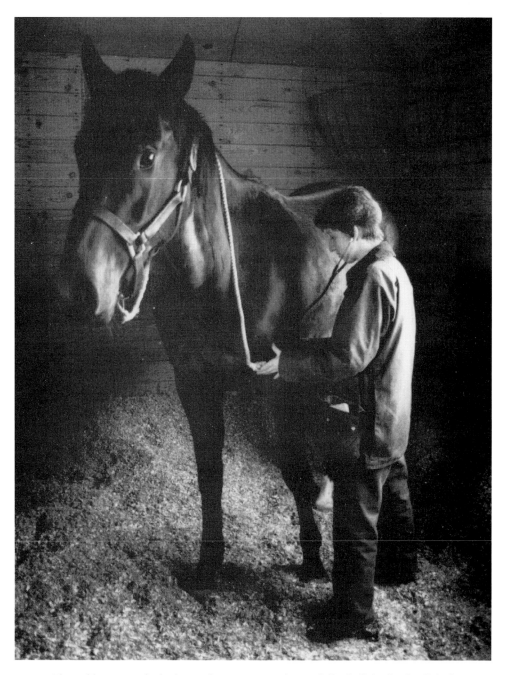

The stables at Langford. The Equine Centre contains specialist facilities for the clinical investigation of respiratory, orthopaedic and cardiac conditions.

about it but is ambivalent, both on grounds of cost and of service to the customers. 'My worry is that if we installed computers we might end up spending more time staring at the screen than addressing the client. I've seen this happen before and I know owners do not like it. They want personal attention.' Fiona nods but says nothing. She does not seem convinced by this argument. It is another subtle, but significant, demonstration that this is a two-way interview. The potential employer is being assessed just as closely as the prospective employee.

Fiona and David then discuss a problem which has an enormous impact on most veterinary practices. Bad debts – people who are reluctant to pay their bills. 'As with just about every practice I know,' says David, 'our debts run at a very high level. At the moment several clients owe us four-figure sums.' He concedes that part of the problem is self-inflicted. 'We're not trained to be business people and rely on someone in the practice having some interest and aptitude in that area. Do you do any training at vet school now?' Fiona shakes her head. 'None whatsoever I'm afraid.'

The interview continues at a nearby farm, where Fiona is asked to carry out a routine check on a frisky young horse. There are some awkward moments as the student makes several attempts to coax the animal into allowing her to examine him for evidence of an undescended testicle. Eventually she succeeds. David is impressed. 'Fiona certainly seems to have had plenty of experience as a student and a real interest and affinity with horses. She seems self-confident and I would imagine her having a good manner with clients, which is very important. Ability is fine, but you need to be able to get clients on your side.'

Fiona is impressed too. She knows Devon well, loves outdoor leisure pursuits and spent several weeks surfing here during her summer holiday last year. David Gabriel knows that the county's natural attractions are another selling-point for his practice. 'We're not short of rural or rustic charm', he tells Fiona as they say their goodbyes. She agrees. 'It is a beautiful area and it sounds like a really good package. The practice has had a recent influx of money and they obviously have some exciting plans for the future.'

However, once the interview is complete and Fiona is heading back to Langford she voices a few reservations. Some of them are personal.

Her parents and her boyfriend live in her home county of Staffordshire and, ideally, she would wish to be close to them. But she also has a few professional concerns. 'I do feel it was a little bit cramped in the surgery, though David acknowledged that himself and was talking about moving to new premises at some point. And one of the surgeries didn't have any customer parking, and that can be a real headache for owners who need to carry their sick animals.' And if she was to be offered a job there? 'I don't know. I'd have to seriously think about it.'

The observations are delivered with tact and diplomacy. She does not wish to shut any doors and it is clear that David Gabriel's practice holds some real attractions. However, it is also clear that the veterinary students are in a seller's market. They are scarce and sought-after commodities, and the interview process will see them asking as many question as they answer. Any veterinary practice that wants to buy them is going to have to compete hard because, after five years of training, the students know their worth.

David Gabriel recognises the state of the market. He says there is such a shortage of British veterinary graduates going into practice that he is having to employ people from overseas. Indeed, he currently has a young New Zealand vet working for him. 'Nothing wrong with that except that they don't usually want to stay. They're here to gain a little experience and earn enough money to do a bit of travelling before they return home.'

Which is exactly what David's New Zealander is planning to do in September. His departure will create the vacancy that Fiona might fill. 'I'm certainly coming round to the view that aptitude is more important than experience, so that's why I'm looking for a bright young graduate', says David Gabriel. 'On the basis that we should have a job in the autumn and that she passes her finals, there is a strong possibility I would offer Fiona that job.'

Whether Fiona would take it is quite another matter. There are plenty of other tempting job offers on the horizon. Already the veterinary trade magazine is full of advertisements aimed at attracting young graduates. Fiona Green and her colleagues have plenty of time and an enviable range of choice.

Surgery

S URGERY IS PERHAPS the most demanding clerking rotation. It will be the first opportunity for the students to take scalpel to skin. The experience is exciting, nerve-racking and unique. All the fifth-year students will have opportunities to spay animals brought in from animal welfare organisations such as the RSPCA. The operations, although supervised, are carried out by the students themselves. Very few other veterinary schools in the country offer this level of hands-on experience.

Several times a week a van arrives with ten animals to be spayed that day. It is a potentially sensitive issue because students are not allowed to operate on people's pets. But – for the time being at least – these dogs and cats are homeless, and it is easy to understand the benefits that flow both to Bristol and to the welfare organisations. The RSPCA gets an expensive operation performed at a considerably reduced fee, while the veterinary school is able to provide invaluable surgical experience for its students.

It is all supervised by the most controversial, talked-about and perhaps most misunderstood figure at the school. To the students he is known simply as 'the Professor.' Professor Harold Pearson, 65 years old and due to retire in the summer, could almost be considered part of the fixtures and fittings. He has been here for 47 years, apart from a 12-month break in the early 1950s.

Professor Pearson came from a farming family in Lancashire and it had been a boyhood ambition to become a vet. He was one of the first group of 25 students when the veterinary school was set up in 1949. The standards and the facilities at the school then left a lot to be desired. 'I have to say the teaching really wasn't very good', he recalls.

'There was very little clinical material to examine and there weren't enough teaching staff. So I do hope things have improved since then.'

An outstanding student, the Professor was always destined for an academic life. After qualifying, he spent just a year as a practising vet in Jersey before returning to Bristol as a teacher, where he has been ever since. He was appointed to his professorship in 1981. 'I chose an academic career because I like the intellectual environment', he says. 'It's a wonderful way to meet other people, staff and students of similar mind.'

Today the Professor, dapper and whippet thin, cuts a distinctive figure around the site. In his office he is an inveterate chain smoker, his large desk clear except for an ashtray and three packets of Rothmans. He is feared by many of the students, disliked by some but respected by most. Their first experience in surgery is always tense, and Professor Pearson has a reputation for being a man of very little patience. He is aware of his reputation and regrets it. A man whose emotions never seem very far from the surface, his fearsome image also clearly upsets him. However, he thinks the problem is not his lack of patience but the students' lack of gratitude. 'I don't think they appreciate all the time I spend with them. I think students have too much influence in schools. There's a trend in universities these days to solicit students' opinions, and many of them take the opportunity to be quite unpleasant. Our job is to help the students, and that's what I try to do.'

Fiona Green knows all about the Professor's reputation and she is preparing for a tense day. It is quarter to seven in the morning and in a few hours' time she will be spaying a cat under his watchful and sometimes unforgiving eye. She is 'knackered' after a late night swotting up on questions the Professor might ask and an early-morning stint typing up case notes from previous clerking duties. 'To make matters worse,' complains Fiona, 'I had a completely exhausting sleep. I was dreaming about drug dosages for cattle. I fear I'm becoming a very sad person!'

Like most of the fifth-year students, Fiona has chosen not to live in the halls of residence. She is acutely aware of the particular pressures posed by being 'stuck out in the country'. While they are in Bristol for the first three years of their course the veterinary students have plenty

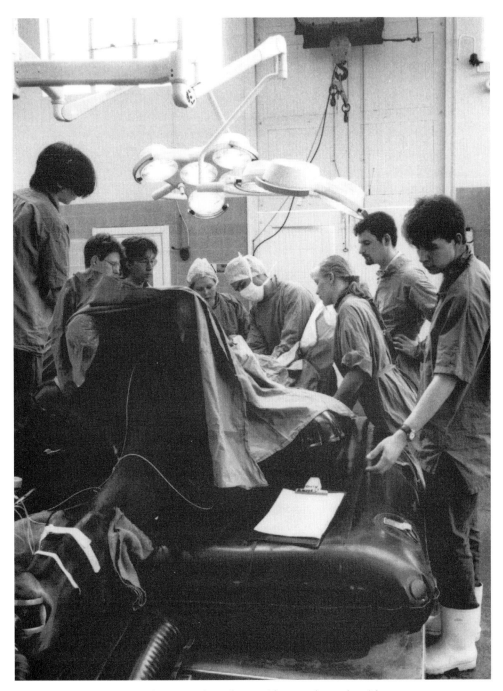

Operating on a 'rig', a horse with an undropped testicle.

of distractions on their doorstep. It is relatively easy to have a life out-side the course and away from colleagues. However, out in Langford there is not a great deal for the young people to do except to concentrate all their academic and social energies on each other. It makes them a very close-knit group, but all the students recognise that it can also be very claustrophobic.

The way most of them choose to find space and escape the pressure-cooker atmosphere is to rent a house off campus. Fiona shares a terraced cottage in the nearby village of Wrington with her dog and cat and fellow student Alison Lee. Alison is reckoned to be one of the brightest students on the course. This morning she is paying particular attention to the news. The government has just conceded for the first time that mad-cow disease could possibly be passed on to humans.

Alison is concerned about the health implications but anxious too that the scare is kept in perspective. 'I think the risks are small compared with everything else we do in life. I'm not going to stop eating beef just yet.'

Fiona, meanwhile, is preoccupied with other things. Before she leaves for surgery she must walk her dog and type up as many of her case notes as she can. She has borrowed a portable word processor from a friend and has to return it in four days. 'There's a real danger as finals approach that things can really get on top of you. I'm always behind, and living with Alison doesn't help. She's so bloody organised, always ahead. It's a constant reminder of my shortcomings.'

In the surgery block Professor Pearson is reflecting on the challenges of surgery. It isn't just the students that worry about spaying an animal. 'I must say the first time they do it, it's very stressful for me. Things can go wrong – a haemorrhage perhaps – and then the animal's life is at risk.'

An operation to spay a cat or dog normally lasts three-quarters of an hour. By law, if students are operating they must be under direct, professional supervision. 'It takes an awful lot of my time', says the Professor – and then, returning to a familiar theme, he adds: 'I think the point I'd like to make is that the students have a unique opportunity for hands-on experience which some of the students don't appreciate.'

In fact most of the students do seem to appreciate that experience. Indeed, many of them cite it as one of the most valuable parts of the whole course. However, what is also undoubtedly true is that some of the students do not welcome the teaching style of the distinguished Professor of Surgery.

Professor Pearson is acutely sensitive to the criticism and is genuinely hurt that he is regularly singled out for particularly harsh lampooning at the students' Christmas pantomime. 'I can't bear to go and haven't been for a very long time. I find some of it very vulgar and very vindictive.'

Such sensitivity works both ways. Some of the students seem to find criticism hard to handle – a legacy perhaps of the enormous praise that must have dominated their schooling until the age of 18. It isn't until they get to the veterinary school that many of them confront failure for the first time and begin to understand their limitations as well as their strengths. Ask the Professor whether he thinks he is too tough with the students and the response is blunt. 'No. My main concern is with the animal's welfare. If something goes wrong, then I've got to put it right. So I've got a duty to the animal and its owner. My duty to the student is of a secondary nature.'

Fiona has arrived at the surgery and is now in the operating theatre, where the atmosphere is tense. As the Professor ties her gown he outlines the task. 'It's a routine operation ... veterinary surgeons perform it every day in practice. But it's got to be done carefully because things can go wrong. The last thing you want is for an animal to die.'

The operation to spay the cat begins with Fiona working on one side of the table and Professor Pearson standing, arms folded, on the other side. He does not touch the animal or handle any of the surgical instruments, but he never takes his eye off Fiona's hands as she works. As he leans forward, peering through thick glasses, their heads are sometimes only inches apart. Inevitably it is intimidating – yet, paradoxically, such close attention can also be very reassuring. The student knows that if something were to go wrong one of the best surgeons in the business is ready to step in immediately and put it right.

The Professor is constantly prompting and, on this occasion, largely encouraging. Fiona is doing a good job. 'Cut a bit towards me ... cut a little deeper ... that's better. Take the forceps and find the uterus ... well done.'

Concentration is etched on Fiona's face and several times she fills her cheeks and lets out a long sigh of tension. Not only is she having to deal with what is going on under her hands right now, but Professor Pearson is constantly firing questions, forcing her to think ahead.

'How are you going to finish the stitch?'

A pause of several seconds while Fiona considers her answer. 'When I get to the end I'll form a loop and take it through three times.'

'That's right. Why is that better than making a knot?'

'Because that way you bury it underneath. It doesn't stick out.'

'Yes.'

The operation is completed to the Professor's satisfaction and the cat, now conscious again, is carried to a recovery room. A clearly elated Fiona reflects on a job well done. 'Absolutely wonderful. Normally the uterus is buried away and you can't find it. But I just opened it up and there it was.'

Aside from the technical details, she has also avoided a confrontation with her teacher. Indeed, he appears to have been quietly impressed. 'I survived the wrath of the Professor', she laughs. 'He never shouted at me. The atmosphere in there was a little tense to say the least. When you've got the Professor standing over you and asking questions you start to sweat and your hands start to shake. But it was ok.'

Like all the students at this stage in the year, Fiona is beginning to think beyond the clerking rotations and forward to a career as a qualified vet. She is growing in confidence, revealing that she might have done things a little differently had the Professor allowed her more latitude. 'It will be nice doing it without someone looking over your shoulder. Not long now.'

But as Fiona Green contemplates the beginning of a career, Professor Harold Pearson is reflecting on the end of one. His retirement will coincide with the students' graduation. After nearly half a century at the veterinary school it is clearly going to be very difficult breaking the ties.

Retirement is a difficult matter to raise with the Professor. It is an emotive issue for him and, in the privacy of his office, the man who arouses so much apprehension and fear among students suddenly appears vulnerable. As he reflects on his career he is frequently close

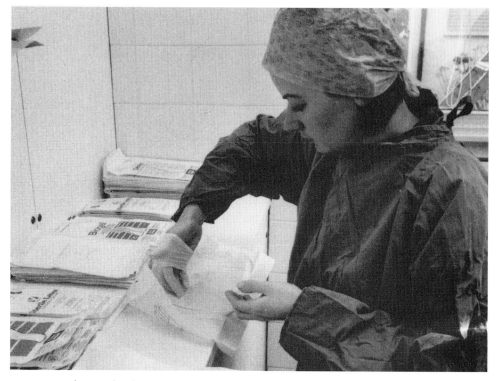

Above and right, Fiona Green prepares to take scalpel to skin for the first time.

to tears. Professor Pearson does not want to leave. He has to because, at the age of 65, he must retire – it is a university rule.

He talks in short, measured sentences about why he enjoys the job so much. Yes, he loves the environment, the animals and the intellectual challenge, but he also insists that one of the main attractions is the contact with students. He appears to be genuinely mystified and upset by his unpopularity and brushes aside suggestions that he is an intimidating figure. The Professor's line is that he does what he has to do. 'My intention is to make sure that when the students graduate they perform competently because I shan't be there to help them if things go wrong.'

Some of the students may regard his absence as a huge blessing. Perhaps, though, Professor Pearson is right when he says they are too young to appreciate what he does for them. There is no doubt that he is a man who cares deeply about standards in his profession and the

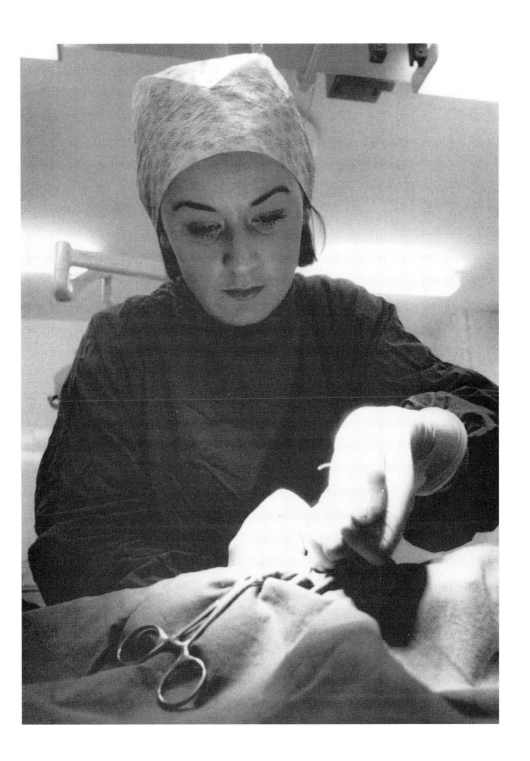

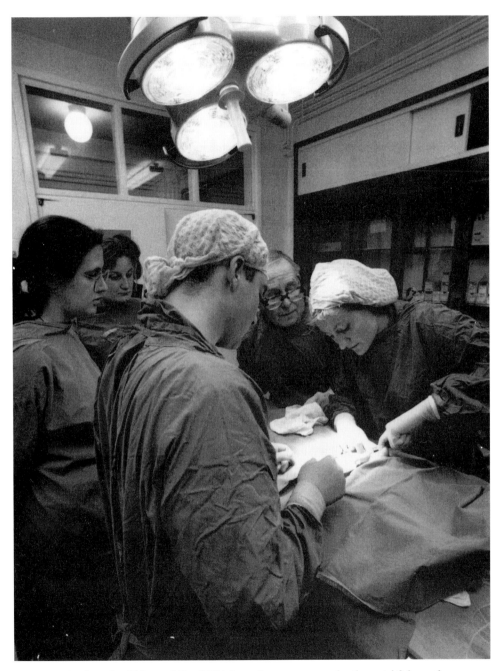

Students Pat Ridge and Carol Wright perform surgery under the watchful eye of Professor Pearson.

next generation of vets who must preserve those standards. He also speaks of his admiration for the students, proudly pointing out that 'they're better qualified and cleverer each year'.

Many of those who struggle have felt the lash of his tongue. However, some of the strugglers have had good reason to thank the greatly misunderstood Professor of Surgery. Those who fail their finals are usually given the opportunity to resit the exams. But not immediately. After five years at university many have substantial debts. They are banking on qualifying and being able to start earning a salary immediately. Deprived of that opportunity, the debts may be too much to manage.

In previous years this is where Professor Pearson has stepped in. 'When students do fail,' he says, 'I usually ask them if they have any financial problems that I can help with.' The details have to be coaxed from him but, even then, he remains vague, apparently embarrassed to reveal such a personal interest in his students' affairs. 'On three or four occasions I have made funding available, but I don't want to say any more than that. It would be inappropriate.'

The Professor is very stiff and proper, refusing to talk about any students by name – either those he has helped or those who have directed personal criticism at him. His constant gripe is a more general one … that young people take things for granted. It is not surprising, therefore, that when he is asked to describe his favourite students he declines to name individuals but returns to a familiar theme. 'The students I like best are the ones who come to me at the end of the year and say, "Thank you very much for the training. I really enjoyed it."'

Social life

'Social life. What social life?' This is the standard veterinary student response to any inquiry about their leisure time. It is certainly true that in the fifth year the demands of the clerking system tend to upset any equilibrium that might exist between time in and time out.

However, the biggest problem facing the students is a logistical one. Rural Somerset has much to commend it – but not if you are in your early twenties and want to play as hard as you work. In their first three years in the city of Bristol the students have clubs, pubs, concerts and restaurants on their doorstep. In their last two years at Langford they have the student bar, occasional vet-school concerts, and discos and village pubs. The city may never sleep at night, but the country-side most certainly does. It is very difficult to find anything to do after 11 p.m.

Most of the students own old cars, but they are reluctant to drive into Bristol for a night out. Drinking is one of their favourite occupations and none of them is stupid enough to risk drinking and driving. A vet without a driving licence is going to find it very difficult to earn a living. And even if they could still find employment, they would automatically deprive themselves of one of the prime perks of the job – a free car.

Public transport is not really an option either. Buses are infrequent at the best of times and virtually non-existent in the evenings. There is no train service, and a return taxi trip into Bristol costs in the region of £32, way beyond what any of the students can afford. So they are stranded in Langford and the surrounding villages, a cause of enormous frustration to many of them.

It is certainly curious that the veterinary school was built so far away from the university city of Bristol. It is possible to drive just a few miles out of the centre and find enough 'countryside' to give the students the practical experience they need. Indeed, the Head of the Veterinary School at Langford, Professor Philip Duffus, concedes that it would suit everyone better to be closer to Bristol. In particular, he recognises the social problems posed by the site's isolation. 'I don't think our average student has a lot of social life outside what goes on in Langford. During their final year we ask a hell of a lot of them. Combine that fact with the location and you can appreciate why they have difficulties. I think it's a pity we are situated so far out.'

However, when the University was looking for a greenfield space on which to build the school just after the war, Langford was the first suitable site to become available. Students with their own cars are a relatively new phenomenon. One can only assume that in the past they must have felt even more isolated.

So they probably did then what they do now. Go to the pub. 'Certainly a lot of their social lives seems to revolve around pubs. But I see no problem with that', says Professor Duffus. 'There are some great country pubs around here and a lot of us like going to them.'

Today's students have a particular favourite. In fact the 'Golden Lion' in Wrington is more than a favourite. It is really the only pub in the area they use – the beginning, the middle and the end of most nights out.

Wrington is a pretty village but, more important from the students' point of view, it is a big village with some facilities. Two and a half thousand people live there, including many of the trainee vets. It is just two miles from the veterinary school and has a small supermarket, a delicatessen, a newsagent, an off-licence and two pubs. Every summer the local post-office window is full of notices from students looking for houses to rent. Wrington is their home during the final year.

The relationship with the Golden Lion goes back many years. The landlord clearly values their custom and even hangs photos of previous graduates on his walls. Last year's final-year students had their farewell party there, and there wasn't a dry eye in the house. 'It was a very emotional evening', says Mike Thorne. 'They were all lovely people who did us proud in the local pub.' As a thank you he put them all up free of charge for the night. They reciprocated with a 'huge bunch of flowers for my wife. Smashing people.'

Mike thinks just as highly of the present bunch. 'They enjoy a laugh and a drink and just use us as their community meeting point.' Tonight it is a bitterly cold March evening and about a quarter of the final-year students are meeting for a drink. All are involved in busy clerking weeks, so none of them arrive before 10 p.m.

A few are playing a game of pool, but most are slumped in chairs, clutching pints, looking exhausted and worrying about exams. Pat Ridge, who has previously revelled in his reputation as a party animal, claims he is now a reformed character. No more behaving badly for him. Instead he has now recast himself as a sober, sensible student. The reason? 'Exams. You can look at it one of two ways. You could say it's only March, we've got three months to go – and it sounds like a very long time. Or you could say we've only got nine or ten weeks, which sounds quite terrible actually.'

Even the most able students are beginning to feel the pressure. Alison Lee has not had to reform herself. She has worked consistently hard and has always achieved some of the best results in her year. However, the occasional sense of claustrophobia, which is never far from the surface in the close-knit, isolated world of the vet school, is beginning to make itself felt as finals approach. 'Everyone starts getting ratty with their friends', says Alison. 'I'm looking forward to the Easter holidays now because a change is as good as a rest. Even though we know we're going to go home and revise, at least you get to see your family, get your head round some other things and chill out a bit. And hopefully we'll all come back refreshed.'

The refreshments on offer in the Golden Lion are consumed with alacrity. The drinking is accompanied by much smoking and a lengthy conversation about the best methods of revision. Who has the best system? Is there such a thing as a system? They all appear to have different tactics, but they agree that the practical nature of the final year has made it easier to retain crucial information. Textbook learning has a way of going in one ear and out the other, particularly when it comes to complicated subjects like anatomy.

Pat Ridge's formula for revising for finals consists of writing practice essays. But that doesn't work for Alison Lee. She has to read and re-read notes. 'It appeared to be easier to remember stuff when I was doing my A levels', she recollects. 'I think some brain cells must have died over the last five years. Basically, we all need to do as much revision as we can over the Easter holidays.'

At the pool table Jon Coupe is playing it cool. 'I went through a period a couple of weeks ago when I was completely stressed by the prospect of finals. But I'm ok now.' He may be ok, but when you live, work and play with others who are all studying for the same degree, all have the same preoccupations and are all facing the same pressures it is difficult to avoid talking shop.

Around closing time the group begins a heated debate about the lecturers. Inevitably, two names dominate a conversation that is increasingly lubricated by alcohol: Professor Harold Pearson and Dr Kieran O'Brien. Jon Coupe is not a fan of 'the good doctor', although he does concede that Kieran is an accomplished teacher. 'He knows his stuff, but he has a lot of opinions which would have been more appropriate 50 or 60 years ago. It's not his teaching that is a problem but his attitude.'

Like most of the students, Jon is aware that one student in particular has found Dr O'Brien difficult to handle. 'Trude Mostue has had a really bad run with Kieran. He hasn't done enough to build her confidence. She knows her stuff three or four times better than I do, but she thinks she's not worthy in some way.'

However, many of the other students are much more complimentary. They argue that he's an excellent teacher who they can also have a good laugh with. Pat Ridge describes him as 'that nice Irish bloke who gave me a decent grade'. Alison Lee, who is thinking of applying for a job as O'Brien's houseman after she has graduated, is a fan too. 'He's full of useful tips and I think he's really nice. It's true that he tries to wind you up from time to time, but as long as you don't let it get to you he's fine really.'

The students' verdict on Professor Pearson is that he is a distinguished surgeon and academic, capable of great kindness but also prone to critical outbursts which can destroy the confidence of some students. Pat Ridge says: 'He's taught me a lot. I think he was probably a brilliant surgeon in his time, but I don't think he knows how to deal with today's students.'

Alison Lee, Fiona Green, Steve Leonard and Pat Ridge share a joke.

Jon Coupe, so critical of Dr O'Brien, is rather impressed by the Professor. 'He's all right to me – pleasant and kind. I think we're lucky to have such a world-renowned surgeon. Having said that, though, I do know he's ripped a few people apart. He seems to be very nasty to women at times.'

The allegation of a gender bias switches the talk to an indisputable gender imbalance on the course. About 75 per cent of the fifth-years are women and in other years there are proportionately even more females. Why? No one really knows the answer, but a consensus of a kind begins to emerge among tonight's drinking partners. They reckon that women mature more quickly and the impression is that perhaps they work harder. In a typically outspoken manner Jon Coupe risks alienating three-quarters of his colleagues by openly worrying about this trend: 'They're all likely to get pregnant around the same time and then we'll have a real shortage of vets'.

It's the kind of tortured logic that bars up and down the country seem to inspire and it is simply ignored. Jon has opinions about lots of things, and the next one he throws in for consideration attracts more

Making the most of it. Jon Coupe and Pat Ridge enjoy the finer things in life.

sympathy. 'I still love animals, but not in the way I did before I began the course. You just can't practise like that. In the five years I've been here I reckon I've lost between 60 and 70 per cent of my compassion.' No one else seems keen to put a figure on compassion loss, but all accept that clerking rotation has been bringing them face to face with economic realities.

Alison Lee contrasts an affluent farmer who came into the small-animal practice with a very sick sheepdog and said, 'Save him – money no object' with a pet owner whose five-year-old labrador was referred to Langford for treatment. 'The owner simply said, "If it's going to cost more than a hundred pounds, just kill it". That was pretty hard to take.'

At closing time the group stumble out as they had arrived – together. Even in their slightly inebriated state they are absorbed in each other and still focused on their course and the career they have chosen. It is not that the students do not know how to have fun but simply that for now they are all working towards one goal – their finals.

Studying for a veterinary degree, particularly in the fifth year, does not lend itself to distractions. In this respect their isolation in the countryside can be beneficial. As Jon Coupe ruefully remarks as he makes his way along the pavement: 'There's bugger-all else to do out here, so we might as well work.'

If they are resigned to hard work rather than a wild social life, Professor Philip Duffus will not be complaining. Not that he is a killjoy, but the Head of the Veterinary School at Langford does not want the students he so patently admires to become distracted as they approach the home straight. 'They've got a hell of a lot of revision to do. An enormous amount of revision, and they mustn't lose sight of that.'

What social life the students do have tends to come in small, unscheduled and concentrated bursts between clerking rotations. Clerking duties play havoc with activities like organised sport. Team sports are basically out, and many students have had to give up representing the University when they moved out to Langford for the last two years of the course.

However, the Bristol Veterinary School does what it can to accommodate students who are determined to continue with leisure activities despite the pressure of time. Three years ago one of them was among the country's leading up-and-coming event riders. So his exams were rearranged to allow him to attend Badminton and a number of other major international events. Even so it involved a punishing routine, often starting at the crack of dawn. 'God knows how he did it and also found time to fit in his clerking and lectures', says Professor Duffus. 'But somehow he did manage it. Won a few competitions *and* passed his finals.'

For most of the students, though, a social life consists of pubs in the company of fellow veterinary students and, sometimes, their teachers. Often the junior staff are not much older than the pupils, and romantic relationships are not always exclusively between fellow students. It is inevitable that in the pressure-cooker atmosphere at Langford close ties will be forged.

Alison Lee will soon be marrying a vet who qualified from the course last year. But many of the romantic entanglements appear to have a much shorter shelf-life, their foundations perhaps built on the shifting sands of geographical isolation and limited choice. In the main the Langford students appear genuinely to enjoy each other's company, but they all recognise that since they left Bristol there have been times of real academic and social claustrophobia.

'I thing it can get quite incestuous, actually', observes Philip Duffus. 'I often tell members of staff that I think it's important for them not to live too close to Langford because I think they've got to have their own life outside.' The students, he argues, at least have the prospect of 'escape' during their holidays.

However, Professor Duffus is generally in favour of the close social ties that bind some of his staff and students. 'They seem to socialise quite happily even at times of real stress for the students. It's an odd social structure I suppose, really, where one group of people approaching their exams feel torn to pieces by the pressure effectively applied by the other group. When students socialise with staff they might find themselves meeting the people who are putting them through the torture. But, somehow, it all seems to work.'

Charity work

Jon Coupe's next clerking rotation will take him out of the Somerset countryside and into one of Bristol's less affluent suburbs. He and Mike Sandiford are to spend a week in Brislington at the People's Dispensary for Sick Animals.

The PDSA is a charity that provides veterinary treatment for sick and injured pets whose owners cannot afford private fees. For the students it provides a vivid contrast with the brand new small-animal hospital at Langford, its specialist cases and relatively well-off clients.

The PDSA first opened a clinic in Bristol in July 1937 and now treats over 31,000 cases a year. Many of those who turn to the charity for help are elderly and living alone. They are often particularly dependent on their pet for company and affection. Others go there when they have financial difficulties and simply cannot afford private treatment for their sick pet.

The PDSA's veterinary centres will treat up to a maximum of three pets per eligible owner. To be eligible, owners must provide proof that they are householders in receipt of one or more of the standard means-test benefits. However, regardless of the owner's circumstances, emergency cases will always receive an initial diagnosis.

Pet owners do make voluntary contributions, but inevitably their donations are usually far less than the actual cost of the treatment. At the moment the average contribution is 77 pence, while the cost of providing a single treatment is £10.03. The shortfall has to be made up by local appeals, legacies, the sale of goods and income from PDSA shops.

Most of the patients treated are domestic pets. Seventy-one per cent are dogs, 24 per cent cats and the remainder, classified as exotic pets, include birds, small caged animals and reptiles.

*Woman's best friend. Patient and owner wait for treatment
in the small-animal hospital.*

Jon Coupe's first case is an 'exotic'. He is not on top form this morning, though he has put on a tie to present a businesslike appearance to the public. Yesterday he played rugby for the first time in a couple of years and injured his back. 'I feel like I should be in bed', he complains. 'I can't bend over and ought to be in a doctor's surgery, not a veterinary practice.'

After a sleepless night Jon is still grimacing from the pain. His discomfort only increases when he spies Willard. Willard is a rat, and he has just been brought into one of the consulting rooms by his owner, Mrs Julia Everett. He is rather large and, for the moment, still in his cage. Jon begins the consultation with an exaggeratedly businesslike approach that could best be described as brusque. His first words to the client are brief and direct. 'Ok, what's the problem?' Mrs Everett looks a bit non-plussed.

At this point the supervising PDSA veterinary officer, Eamon Draper, steps forward from the back of the room and makes a suggestion. 'It might be a good idea to introduce yourself.'

'Ah yes. My name is Jon and I'm from the vet school in Langford.'

This is a key moment in Jon Coupe's training. Like most of the students he knows his science, but Eamon takes the view that the week of clerking at the PDSA is about teaching students the art of veterinary practice. In other words it is not only about showing what they know, it is also about displaying the social skills that are so important when dealing with clients. As Eamon observes later: 'You are treating the owners just as much as you are treating the patients'.

For now, though, Jon has got through the introductions and has switched his attention to the patient. Willard has a swelling on his eye. He has been to the surgery before but, despite a prescription of antibiotics, the swelling continues to grow. Jon has stared at him in his cage long enough. It is time to get Willard out for a closer look – though not before a couple of questions to Mrs Everett. 'How is he handling? Is he particularly vicious at all?' The owner smiles reassuringly. 'He's fine, very friendly.'

Willard is a little reluctant to come out of his cage. When Jon puts his hand inside and takes hold of him the animal clings to the bars. After a bit of gentle tugging he is prised out, blinking, into the bright lights of the consulting room.

Jon Coupe the student and Willard the rat make eye contact. The room is very quiet. Eamon Draper has stepped back again and Mrs Everett is looking to Jon for answers. After a long pause he begins to make some routine inquiries about the animal's general state of health. Is he eating normally? How are his waterworks? Has he shown any signs of being in pain? Everything is fine, says Mrs Everett, apart from the swelling over his eye.

After this short exchange there is another very long pause while Jon stares at the rat and the rat stares back. Willard does indeed have a very nasty-looking swelling over his eye, but Jon is clearly puzzled as to the cause. The awkward silence continues. It is becoming embarrassing and the student vet is struggling to project an air of confidence. He knows that if he does nothing else, he has to engage the owner in conversation and lift the hush that has descended on the room and is now beginning to dominate the consultation. 'Do you feed him on dry food?' he manages. Mrs Everett laughs. 'Well, sometimes. But mostly we give him ham, toast, bacon and scrambled egg.' 'Oh', says Jon, and the silence is restored.

Jon stares even more intently at the rat. But no matter how hard he looks no answers appear to be forthcoming, and when he begins repeating some of the questions he has asked Mrs Everett only a few minutes before, Eamon Draper steps in. 'I think we had better go outside and confer.'

Jon is biting his lip and scratching his head as Eamon asks for his diagnosis. He doesn't know whether the swelling is a cyst or an abscess, or what has caused it. He does know that a previous course of antibiotics hasn't worked. 'So, where should we go from here?' Eamon asks. 'What about giving the rat a general anaesthetic and taking a closer look?' suggests Jon. It is a fairly drastic suggestion at this stage and the PDSA veterinary officer is not persuaded. It would be an expensive and risky course of action. It is all too easy to give small animals a fatal overdose, and if they do not give Willard enough anaesthetic he could wake up during the operation.

Eamon believes the swelling may be caused by a 'foreign body', a small object that has worked itself into the skin. If they are lucky, Willard may dig it out himself. In the meantime he decides that they should try a more potent antibiotic. 'When should we expect to see him again?' asks Eamon and, before Jon can respond, suggests the answer: 'Presumably when another student is on duty'. Both of them laugh, recover their composure and return to Mrs Everett to deliver their diagnosis and course of treatment. She will give Willard a course of stronger antibiotics and return in ten days.

By then, Jon Coupe will have returned to the vet school. It has been an instructive morning for him. Eamon Draper believes that the clerking system is enormously beneficial and improving all the time. 'Things have changed a lot even since I was at vet school. They're taught a lot more about the practical side these days, and what we can do for them at the PDSA is to teach them the social skills that are required. In the past it was just very much "learn the disease and develop everything else when you're out in practice".'

Despite Jon's discomfort during his first consultation, Eamon declares himself impressed by the student's level of knowledge. He says that everyone they have had from the Bristol Veterinary School has been bright, competent and confident. They know their veterinary science. What most of them are not so good at is relating to and empathising with the clients. 'As you would expect, they are very much into lecture-based material. So they see cases from a clinical point of view and they don't know what to do if a client bursts into tears.'

The communication point is taken up by Eamon's boss, Senior Veterinary Officer Ruth Lloyd. She sees the PDSA as an opportunity for students to practise what they will be doing when they go into their first jobs – consulting one to one with clients. 'They have to speak to owners in more basic terms than they would at university, where they're talking to other students and academic staff in very scientific terms. It's really quite tricky trying to bring problems down to an everyday level for owners to understand.'

The clerking week at the PDSA also introduces students to more 'everyday' kind of cases. The atmosphere at Langford is a rarefied one, both intellectually and clinically. At the school they tend to see complicated cases requiring a second opinion that have been referred by a private vet. Students would be expected to work them up to the 'full degree', using blood tests, X-rays and all the other investigative procedures to get to the bottom of the problem.

'When you're in practice,' says Ruth Lloyd, 'you have to recognise that common problems occur and not go over the top with them. For example, flea allergies, kennel cough and ear infection you would treat symptomatically rather than running a whole load of tests, which would be very expensive.'

The PDSA experience is clearly invaluable for the students, but watching them grope their way to a diagnosis and treatment can be a time-consuming business. So what is in it for the society? The People's Dispensary for Sick Animals may be a registered charity, but its enthusiastic backing for the clerking system is not motivated by any particularly charitable concerns for either the veterinary school or its students. It is much more a calculated and hard-headed business decision.

Some direct benefits flow immediately to the organisation. In exchange for the PDSA's cooperation, the University does a lot of the charity's lab work free of charge. But there is a longer-term and more important calculation in all this. It needs to compete for tomorrow's veterinary talent just the same as the private practices. Inviting them in on what amounts to a work-experience programme can be a pretty effective way of doing this. Both Eamon Draper and Ruth Lloyd spent time at the PDSA during their veterinary degree courses.

Ruth remembers it well. 'It was an enjoyable experience and helped to build up my confidence because it was the first time I was allowed to do consultations by myself. It was supervised in that, at the end of a consultation, a qualified vet would always have to come and check the animal and check that you were doing the right things with it. But you were actually given the responsibility of examining an animal, taking a history, trying to work out what the diagnosis might be and considering appropriate treatment.'

Traditionally, the People's Dispensary for Sick Animals has been regarded as one of the less attractive jobs for young graduates. Although it is competitive on pay, facilities in some of the surgeries have had a reputation for being below average. That is changing. The Bristol PDSA was extensively refurbished in 1993 and now boasts a new waiting room, five consulting rooms, a reception area, dispensary, theatre preparation area, two theatres, recovery wards, a staff room and a drug room.

Ruth, who arrived two years ago after a spell in private practice, says facilities at the PDSA are now generally above average. The students, though, need to experience that first-hand. They know they are going to be able to pick and choose after graduation, and all potential employers are now having to sell themselves. Indeed, in future years the PDSA is hoping to make formal presentations at veterinary schools in the hope of attracting students away from private practice.

However, she acknowledges that the most effective way for the PDSA to demonstrate the range of its work is to allow Langford's fifth-year students to come in and 'have a go', just as she did when a student. She says it is usually a positive experience for everyone concerned. 'They're all very bright and spend a lot of the week asking us some very pertinent questions. It keeps us on our toes.'

The clients do not seem to mind either. It means their pets get extra attention because the students are asked to do a full clinical examination of the animal. And the PDSA knows that the students themselves find it stimulating because they are asked to deliver a verdict when they have completed the clerking rotation. 'The students have to report back at the end of their week here – and they assess us as well as us assessing them', says Ruth Lloyd. 'They're usually very positive about it and appreciate the wide range of experience and responsibility we give them.'

Student Mike Sandiford, who has joined Jon Coupe on the PDSA clerking week, is about to experience one of a vet's most onerous responsibilities. While Jon is discharging a young, relatively fit rat, in an adjacent consulting room Mike is admitting a very sick old rabbit. 'Bunny' is ten years old and cannot move her back legs.

Bunny's owner, Mrs Scrase, is upset, but Mike Sandiford appears to be handling them both well. Eamon Draper walks into the room. 'What's the story with the rabbit?' 'She came in a week ago with partial paralysis and isn't getting any better', says Mike.

The two excuse themselves and confer in the corridor. They know, as does the owner, that they may have to put Bunny to sleep. A course of steroids has failed to have any effect and ten years is a good age for a rabbit. However, they are not ready to make a decision just yet and want to talk a little more to Mrs Scrase. In a moment of unintentional

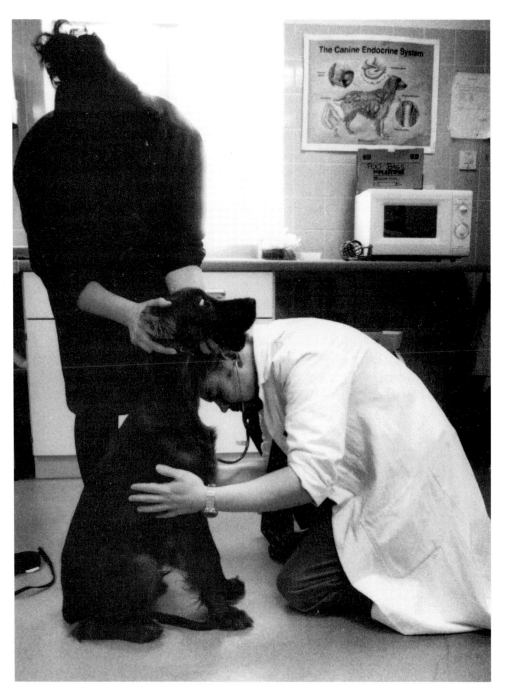

Listen carefully. Jon Coupe and patient are all ears.

humour Eamon looks at Bunny, turns to Mike and says 'I think we should just play this one by ear for a few minutes'.

When they go back into the consulting room the owner says she is worried about the rabbit's poor quality of life. 'She seems very floppy. This morning when she tried to wash herself she fell over. It would have been comic if it hadn't been so sad.'

'Is she still eating well?' asks Eamon.

'Yes, she's got a lovely appetite. But she's also very thirsty', says Mrs Scrase.

'Why would that be?' asks Eamon, directing the question at Mike. The student is unable to produce an immediate answer, but after a few seconds he remembers. 'Oh yes, because of the steroids.'

Eamon is reluctant to try steroids again and realises that the options are running out for Bunny. He also knows that Mrs Scrase does not want to put the rabbit through any more unnecessary trauma.

Everyone knows where the conversation is leading, but this is new territory for Mike Sandiford and Eamon's question to him is a difficult one. 'Is the quality of life too low to try another treatment?' Mike shoots a nervous glance at the owner, who is stroking Bunny and looking increasingly upset. 'It depends what the owner thinks, really. I would like to try another treatment as the rabbit is obviously getting a lot of love and care.' The student pauses. 'But I wouldn't know what to try.'

Neither does Eamon. He steps forward to the examination table, where Bunny has remained quite still for several minutes, strokes her and then says gently to the owner. 'I think we'd better call it a day.' Mrs Scrase nods her agreement. 'I was expecting that', she sighs. Eamon reassures her that the decision is the right one. 'Although she isn't in a terrible state right now, I think that if we leave her another week that's what might happen.'

Mike puts the rabbit back into her box and continues to stroke her as the owner signs a consent form. Eamon explains that he will give the rabbit an overdose of anaesthetic and that she will just drift off to sleep and never wake up. 'It's not painful and it won't take long.'

Bunny will be carried to another room where she will be put to sleep, but not before Mrs Scrase has told Mike that she wants to take the rabbit home and bury her. 'She's one of the family you know.

I don't want to leave her here; I want to bury her in the garden next to Scamp, our cat.'

Eamon and Mike pick Bunny up and tell the owner they will only be a couple of minutes. Mrs Scrase is now alone in the consulting room. Although upset she is also composed and, in a way, relieved. Over the last few weeks she has been watching the rabbit grow weaker and more dependent. She had not wished to watch Bunny deteriorate further. Mrs Scrase has two other elderly family pets as well, a 17-year-old cat and a 10-year-old dog. 'I suppose it makes you realise that we're all growing old together', she muses sadly. 'I'm really going to miss Bunny.'

Eamon Draper and Mike Sandiford return to the consulting room with the rabbit. She has been wrapped in a towel and returned to her cardboard box, which is handed back to Mrs Scrase. It is a sad moment for the owner and a rather awkward one for the young student. Mike avoids eye contact with Mrs Scrase and, by now, is taking a back seat in proceedings. Understandably it is the experienced vet, Eamon, who has taken control of the situation. 'She went very peacefully', he says gently and reassuringly. 'She wasn't actually that strong. I think she had just been putting a brave face on it.' Mrs Scrase thanks them for their help and kindness and leaves with tears in her eyes.

Helping to put his first patient to sleep has made it a tough start to Mike Sandiford's week at the PDSA. Nevertheless, the experience is an important one, requiring the vet to weigh up the pros and cons of what is always going to be a delicate and difficult decision. Euthanasia is something vets have to consider that doctors do not. The decision to take a life, says Eamon, is never easy, but the thought that an animal is being spared further suffering makes the decision easier to live with. 'It is something which most vets spend quite a lot of time thinking about and something that we have to do quite frequently. It never makes it easy, though. It's always an unpleasant part of the job.'

Mike Sandiford nods his agreement. He knew that sooner or later he would have to confront a case like this and realise that in the future he will deal with many more. He is reconciled to it. 'I think quality of life is the most important thing. As a vet I think euthanasia is a good thing.'

Young vets can be trained in the classroom to make these kinds of decision. Mike knows the scientific and ethical criteria in theory.

But what a lecture cannot prepare them for is how to handle and empathise with a grieving owner. Mike explains that for him the true value of the clerking week is experiencing real life-and-death decisions, dealing with real people, watching a practising vet at work – and listening, too, for the little phrases that might help to soften the blow for owners. 'The vet school doesn't give us any training in counselling the owner', he tells Eamon. 'You only get a sense of it from seeing practice like this. We have had a lot of training about when to consider putting an animal down, but it is not always terribly useful when you're faced with an owner in distress.'

Eamon agrees that there is no substitute for experience. 'You can't give people this sort of training out of a textbook. I can still remember my first euthanasia, a cat with kidney failure. It was very distressing for the owner and myself.'

For a student, putting an animal to sleep can be a particularly awkward experience. If an owner is terribly upset and begins to cry, the qualified vet is part of the experience – there to help them and their pet through the distress. However, as Mike Sandiford sensitively remarks, the student could easily be regarded as some kind of dispassionate voyeur intruding on private grief. 'The owner knew that for me it was just a learning experience, and there were several times when that made me feel I just wanted to melt into the wall.'

Mike's next case will have a happier outcome. Eamon has left him alone in the consulting room to deal with Robson and Jerome. They are guinea pigs, and their owner, who has only had them for a month, has noticed that they have very long teeth – so long, in fact, that they are having difficulty drinking.

Mike is doing a good job, handling the animals and the owner, Robert Lynch, in a confident, friendly manner. 'So you think Robson's the worst?' he asks Mr Lynch. 'Yes. Jerome seems to be ok, but I thought I'd get him checked anyway.

The student lifts Robson out of his cage. The guinea pig bares his teeth helpfully. They are indeed incredibly long, and the top ones are actually cutting into his bottom lip. The teeth do not have any nerves in the end, so Mike suggests a trim. 'I'm just a final-year student, though, so I have to get confirmation of my decision from a qualified vet. Excuse me a minute.'

Mike finds Eamon waiting outside in the corridor. He explains the problem and his suggested solution. Eamon agrees. 'Have you ever clipped teeth before?' 'No', says Mike, a little nervously. 'Well, this will be another first then. Go and get the clippers and we'll give it a go.'

Back in the consulting room Mike introduces Eamon to the client and the guinea pigs. 'Robson and Jerome. Oh dear!' laughs Eamon. 'I wondered when those names would surface.' Mike is now wielding a pair of stainless-steel clippers. A guinea pig's teeth grow constantly, but usually they are kept to length by the animal's natural activities – chief among them eating. But these teeth have now reached such a length that Robson, in particular, is having difficulty either eating or drinking. Eamon tells Mike to trim them down to two or three millimetres. At present they must be six times that length.

'Perhaps when you've done it he'll be a better singer', jokes Mr Lynch. Mike manages a rather unconvincing laugh as he holds Robson firmly against his chest with one hand and with the other clamps the clippers on to the guinea pig's two top teeth. He does not have to squeeze very hard before the teeth snap off and shoot across the room, ricocheting off a stainless-steel bowl with a ping.

'Good,' says Eamon encouragingly, 'now the bottom ones.' At this point Robson, who has been very obliging during the dental surgery on his top teeth, decides he has had enough. He begins to make frightened squeaks and almost manages to wriggle free. Eamon steps in to lend a hand. He holds while Mike trims. The bottom teeth come off easily and Robson, already looking more comfortable, tries an experimental nibble. 'Does that feel a little strange?' Eamon asks the guinea pig. 'I bet it does – but it's going to make your life a whole lot more enjoyable.'

Now it's Jerome's turn, and Mike begins the examination. The second guinea pig's teeth are not nearly as long, but they are still longer than they should be. Mike trims them, this time demonstrating his growing confidence. Robson, Jerome and Mr Lynch depart happily.

'It's important that you get a simple procedure like that out of the way before you go into practice', says Eamon. 'You'd look pretty stupid if confronted with a situation like that and you didn't know what to do.' Mike agrees. 'It's not the most complicated thing I'll ever do, but it's good to get things like that under your belt whilst there is help on hand if you need it. I think I could do that again without too much trouble.'

Eamon Draper is impressed by both of his students. Mike Sandiford and Jon Coupe both pass their clerking week at the PDSA without too much difficulty. He thinks that they both have a good level of knowledge and a real understanding of the basic techniques that they will need in general practice. 'Their social skills improved too, though they weren't there at the start. They breezed in with a certain amount of confidence, but that began to unravel a little when they came face to face with some of the clients.'

There is a huge difference between clerking weeks with small animals at the PDSA and attending to large animals on farms. The caring and counselling side of veterinary practice has to come much more to the fore when vets are dealing with companion animals and their owners. 'If you tell a farmer one of his cows is going to die it might be a bit of a blow, but he certainly isn't going to burst into tears', says Eamon. 'On the other hand, if you tell an owner their dog is going to die, it is very often the case that they will become extremely distressed – and it's part of our job to deal with that.'

The variety of work at mixed practices like the PDSA also poses special challenges to novice vets. 'The rat was a nasty surprise for Jon', observes Eamon. 'It was a species he wasn't confident with. But you've got to be able to adapt very quickly. It's very rare that the perfect textbook case walks through the door. Yesterday I had to deal with a couple of iguanas and a parrot.'

Veterinary-school textbooks are unlikely to dwell in too much detail on iguanas, but their owners neither know nor care about that. They expect the vet to know how to deal with every kind of animal and every kind of problem. The clients are often very demanding in the service they expect and unforgiving of any gaps in a vet's knowledge. 'The first six or twelve months after you graduate can be very daunting indeed', remembers Eamon. 'You're trying to remember millions of facts and deal with hundreds of clients. It is very stressful at times.'

The Bristol PDSA's Senior Veterinary Officer, Ruth Lloyd, agrees. 'The first year is the worst. You've got to really want to do it if you are going to stick at it. It's very badly paid for the hours you work and compared to other professionals like dentists, doctors and lawyers.'

However, Ruth is keen to stress that it is a wonderful job. Predictably, she is also keen to emphasise that the PDSA is a particularly
rewarding veterinary environment to work in. Founded in 1917 by
Maria Dickin, one of the pioneers of the animal welfare movement,
the society has never been busier. From a cellar in London's East End,
the People's Dispensary for Sick Animals has come a long way. Today
there are 48 PDSA centres located in major towns and cities throughout Britain. A total of 1.3 million free treatments are carried out annually by the society on sick or injured animals whose needy owners
qualify for its charitable service.

Some of the centres are seeing a 30 per cent increase in workload
every year. They provide a 24-hour emergency service and the busiest
are responding to more than 300 emergency calls a month. By allowing students like Mike Sandiford and Jon Coupe to become part of the
PDSA service, albeit only for a week, the society is hoping to address
one of its greatest problems – staffing shortages.

'We very much hope that some of the students will consider a
career with us', says Ruth Lloyd. She argues that the PDSA can offer a
competitive salary – and set hours as well. The society's vets work a
38-hour week, which, Ruth says, is much better regulated than in private practice. Long and unpredictable working hours are a recurring
complaint of most qualified vets. 'We can also offer really good experience for new graduates. You're not just doing vaccinations and routine
procedures all the time. There's a much wider variety of cases than in
private practice. I would really sell the idea of a career in the PDSA to
other vets.'

And for good reason. A shortage of qualified vets now poses perhaps the greatest threat to the PDSA's future expansion plans. The
nationwide shortage has been exacerbated by new meat-inspection
regulations from the European Community and the continuing growth
in pet ownership. Increasingly, the People's Dispensary for Sick Animals is having to look abroad to find the staff it needs. Indeed, about a
quarter of the veterinary surgeons it now employs are from continen-
tal Europe or the Commonwealth.

Just a couple of miles from the PDSA's clinic in Brislington is the
Bristol headquarters of the Royal Society for the Prevention of Cruelty

to Animals. The RSPCA is also always on the lookout for newly qualified vets and regularly opens its doors to students on their clerking
weeks.

Grizelda Williams is one of the Society's vets charged with the job
of supervising the bright but inexperienced young men and women
who arrive knowing that this is their best bet for a week of concentrated surgical experience. The RSPCA does far less routine consultation work than the PDSA.

Grizelda, the senior RSPCA vet in Bristol, is an enthusiastic sup-
porter of the clerking weeks, recognising that their absence from her
own education put her at a significant initial disadvantage. Even
though it is only ten years since she qualified from Cambridge, she
detects a definite and important shift in emphasis in the way Britain is
now training its young vets. She says that the most important relationship a vet has is with the client, an idea that is surprisingly difficult
to grasp in the rarefied atmosphere of university life. 'I only spoke to
two or three clients in all my years at University. My first real client
was on my first day out in practice – and it was a fairly horrendous
experience.'

The rarefied atmosphere is not just restricted to the lack of contact
between students and members of the public. It also relates to the
difference between the kinds of case that are dealt with at the veterinary school and at the RSPCA. At Langford they tend to be referrals,
requiring a depth of specialist knowledge far beyond that of a fifth-
year student. Consequently, even when they are told to gown up
for surgery their role is often little more than that of an educated
observer.

The Head of the Bristol Veterinary School at Langford, Professor
Philip Duffus, acknowledges the limited opportunities for getting really
stuck in at the University. 'If they were in a human medical school,
they would get that expertise by becoming junior doctors in a very
structured programme of work in the teaching hospitals. We don't
have that, so once they leave here – clutching that bit of paper which
says I passed – they're out in practice. They may be expected to do
locums immediately, so we have to try and get our students up and
running to the best of our ability.'

The University does provide some 'bread and butter' cases – notably in the small-animal practice, supervised by Alison Blaxter, and the large-animal practice, headed by Kieran O'Brien. But it is the 'charity work' that plugs a lot of the gaps in the students' practical education. 'We offer them a lot on site, but we recognised that it still wasn't enough. So we have gone out of our way to form links with the PDSA and the RSPCA', says Professor Duffus.

He argues that because both organisations provide a free or reduced-price service it is easier to introduce clients to the idea of students being involved in delivering veterinary care. 'To be honest, if you're paying hundreds of pounds for your dog to be referred to Langford, you don't really want a student to be your first point of contact. You want a bit of specialist help. You know we're a teaching hospital, so students are involved, but you're not expecting them to be in the front row.'

At the PDSA and the RSPCA the students *are* in the front row, and there are few complaints from clients. The PDSA is the place where they will deal predominantly with medicine, while at the RSPCA the emphasis is on surgery. 'They're the two arms of veterinary care, and I think the combination works brilliantly', enthuses Professor Duffus.

At the RSPCA the students get to perform a wide variety of minor surgery themselves, though they will always have a supervising vet like Grizelda Williams in attendance. Most of the students are rewarding to teach. But not all. Indeed, Grizelda hints that some adopt a know-it-all attitude that borders on arrogance. 'Some of the Bristol students feel they know how to do a certain technique and don't need anyone else to tell them how to do it. What we try to show them here is that there are different techniques to learn. We're experienced vets here, and if only they're prepared to listen and ask questions we can really help them.'

Thankfully the know-alls are a small minority. Most of the students are like Emma Milne – hungry for experience but acutely aware of their limitations. She is preparing for an 'exotic' experience, which, she candidly admits, is likely to defeat her. 'My next consultation is a bunch of rats from a rat-rescue place. Our exotics lectures at University are minimal, so I might be calling the vet quite soon.'

With that, two staff from the rescue centre are ushered into the consultation room clutching four cages, each containing a rat. 'Hello. I was told there were five', says Emma. 'There are. Vera is up my sleeve', replies one of the workers, struggling to produce the only rat with a name.

The student's clients tell her that they 'love rats ... very intelligent and hugely underrated as pets'. Emma, who has a relaxed, easy manner with her customers and handles the patients with confidence, is happy to reinforce that view. 'Yes they're very nice pets to have. Everyone thinks they're disgusting and stuff, but they're much friendlier than many of the other pets that people keep.'

To anyone who is not a rat fan the condition of the pack on view today might tend to confirm the prejudice that they are 'disgusting' animals. All have been scratching at scabs on their backs. The condition is probably caused by mites, says Emma, and can be treated with a simple injection. She briefly excuses herself to check the diagnosis with Grizelda Williams. Grizelda says Emma is probably right but wants to take a quick look herself. After a brief examination the diagnosis is confirmed, the animals get their injections and they head off back to the rat-rescue centre, now a far more attractive prospect to potential new owners.

Emma's next case follows immediately. It may involve surgery – and certainly involves an animal which she is less fond of than rats. 'Holly' is a ten-week-old dwarf rabbit. 'Rabbits can be quite bad consultations', she explains. 'If their claws are long they can really inflict some nasty scratches. It's also really difficult to pick them up because their back legs are so strong. Sometimes if they kick their legs very hard they can break their backs.'

As it turns out, there is not much danger of that with poor Holly. One of her back legs is badly deformed, the result of some sort of growth disturbance. Emma shows Holly's owner, Glen Treasure, the X-rays. 'You can see how the bone has bowed out. Her kneecap is slipping in and out.' Mr Treasure winces slightly.

Emma asks Mr Treasure to put Holly on the floor of the consultation room so she can see for herself how the rabbit's movement is affected. She scoots round at speed with the deformed leg sticking out at a grotesque right angle. Thankfully it does not appear to trouble her unduly, apart from a slight tendency to make her slide rather than hop round corners. 'Does she have any other problems you've noticed?' asks Emma. 'Well, she doesn't appear to be in any pain if that's what you mean. But I have started to notice recently that she loses her balance sometimes when she is trying to clean herself.'

Mr Treasure explains that he bought the rabbit from a pet shop as a Christmas present for his girlfriend. 'She actually wanted a cat, but as we already have a budgie which flies round the house that didn't seem like a good idea. A rabbit seemed like the next best thing.' It was six weeks before Mr Treasure noticed the problem with Holly's leg, and he immediately brought her to the RSPCA.

After conferring with one of the Society's vets Emma explains that the best option is amputation. Glen Treasure looks concerned. He is worried both about the effect on the rabbit and his own squeamishness. 'The thought of a rabbit with three legs doesn't seem right to me. What will it look like to us – and feel like to her?' 'They do very well after amputation,' says Emma reassuringly, 'and once the fur grows back it will all be very neat indeed. Quite often it takes two looks to even notice that one of the legs has gone.'

Mr Treasure, a gentle and polite man who obviously adores his 'girlfriend's rabbit', is reassured. 'If it's going to help her then I think it should be amputated.' Not straightaway, though. The surgery will not be performed this morning and he will have to return to the RSPCA tomorrow to collect Holly.

The operation is straightforward and successful. In theatre Holly's back leg is amputated and she is left to sleep off the effects of the anaesthetic. Mr Treasure waits anxiously in reception, still insisting that Holly's predicament has touched his partner far more than him. 'I do hope everything will be ok, otherwise my girlfriend will be very upset.'

The rabbit regains consciousness and Emma tells Mr Treasure that he can soon take her home. A smile spreads across his face, and it is time for an overdue and predictable confession. 'Ok, I admit it. We've both really missed her, my girlfriend and me. The house has seemed empty without her. I hope she'll come running up to me when she sees me. My only worry now is that Holly will blame us because her leg is missing.'

Emma points out that the rabbit will probably not even be aware of the fact that she now has three legs instead of four. With that Glen Treasure is led into the consulting room for a reunion. He walks quickly across the room in the direction of a brown cardboard box from which two black ears protrude. Holly is wide awake and ready to demonstrate that, when one of them is not working properly, three good legs are less of a handicap than four.

'I think she recognises me', says Mr Treasure optimistically as the three-legged black dwarf rabbit blinks in the light. 'Will she be able to feel any pain at all?'

'Shouldn't be able to', says Emma brightly. 'It seems like such a major operation, but they usually cope with it really well. Much better than humans.'

Mr Treasure has not yet lifted Holly out of the box. Instead, he is stroking her rather tentatively. He is still worried about seeing or

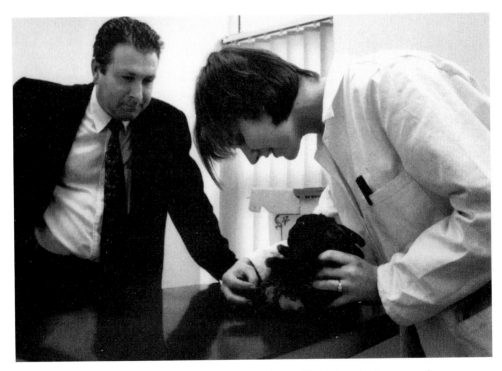

Alison explains to owner Glen Treasure that Holly will need to have one of her legs amputated.

touching the injury. 'Does it look terrible?' 'No, it really doesn't', replies Emma. 'Look, let's just get her out, plonk her on the floor and give her a little run around.' Mr Treasure agrees without much enthusiasm. The rabbit is much more enthusiastic. She hits the floor running and already appears better coordinated and less uncomfortable than before the amputation. 'A new, improved, faster model', laughs the delighted owner as Holly scoots around the consulting room.

It is not easy to recapture her, but once she is safely back in her box Emma tells Mr Treasure that she will adapt quickly to her new three-legged existence. 'All you have to do is to make sure that the wound heals quickly. Don't put her on sawdust while the wound is still open. Hay or newspaper is better until it has closed up. And bring her back in a week for a checkup.'

The mention of open wounds brings an awkward close to the conversation with the squeamish but affable Mr Treasure. 'Ok, yes. But you'll look after all that stuff if there is any trouble, won't you?' 'We will', smiles Emma reassuringly. With that Mr Treasure expresses his thanks and hurries out of the consulting room, afraid, perhaps, that if he stays any longer he might have to stomach a detailed conversation about amputation and its aftermath. Before the door closes behind him Emma and Grizelda can just about hear the beginning of his conversation with the receptionist. 'I need to make another appointment for next week. I reckon Holly is really pleased to be going home. I'm sure she recognised me you know.'

Grizelda and Emma are left alone in the consulting room. For once there is a short break in the seemingly endless string of cases, time to reflect on a week's clerking at the RSPCA and to assess the student's performance.

'How do you think you've got on?' asks Grizelda.

'Well, I've really enjoyed it', replies Emma. 'And I think I've done ok, though I know I've made some mistakes.'

Grizelda nods her agreement before beginning a glowing assessment of Emma's contribution. 'I feel you've come through very well. You're confident and mature enough to discuss things with us and the clients. Sometimes that can be a problem with Bristol students. They lack that ability.'

All this must be music to the ears of a student who, like all her colleagues, has to work incredibly hard to even satisfy the teachers. Impressing them is tougher and rarer still. But from Grizelda there is more praise to come. 'Your techniques have consistently improved. I've been very impressed. There have been occasions at the end of a clerking week when I've thought, thank goodness the student is going. In your case, though, I'm thinking it would be nice to have you back next week.'

This is praise indeed – an official declaration that not only has Emma obviously learnt something but that she has also been useful. It is clerking at its most productive, where the student is able to give as well as take something.

For Emma the week has also produced a glimpse of the near future, an opportunity to have a real taste of a career she chose nearly five years ago. One of the frustrations expressed by many of the students is that, having made the decision to be a vet at perhaps 18 years of age, there are precious few opportunities for hands-on involvement until they are 22.

The first three years of the course at Bristol are designed to be pre-clinical and, inevitably, are biased towards lectures and textbook learning. However, in the fourth year – when they move to Langford for the first of two clinical years – there is the tantalising prospect of some real veterinary experience. 'Tantalising' about sums it up for Emma Milne, who believes that the penultimate year of the course simply does not deliver what it appears to promise. 'The fourth year was such a big disappointment. The subjects were so boring. I just got really demoralised because when you get to vet school all you want to do is to get in there and be a vet. And then you hardly touch an animal for the first four years. It's really hard to see the light at the end of the tunnel. But the fifth year at Bristol – particularly the clerking – is brilliant. Everything begins to click into place.'

Grizelda Williams understands the frustrations, but she believes the University has got the mix right. Of course all the students want to get their hands on the animals as quickly as possible, she says, but they have to be taught a great deal before they are competent enough to be let loose on the public and their animals.

Emma listens carefully and concedes that there is probably no other

*It's not much fun for patients in intensive care, but it does allow students
to put theory into practice.*

way. However, she has another, familiar gripe – and one that Grizelda
echoes. It is the one about the focus on academic excellence as a
method for selecting students for veterinary school. Both women are
concerned about clever children being targeted as potential vets simply
because they are bright.

Grizelda says veterinary practice has to be a vocation or graduates
will not stay with it. Some of her own contemporaries at Cambridge
have long since left the profession to become accountants, lawyers and
drug reps. 'The problem for some people is that they actually find out
it is far less academically demanding than they had expected. The truth
is that a lot of it is very mundane. You look at animals' teeth. You perform spaying operations, which become very routine. And the glam-
orous expectations of the job can dissipate fairly rapidly.'

Yet the romantic ideal of the vet persists in this country, a potent
reminder that we remain a nation of animal lovers. As long as we love

our pets, how can we do anything other than cherish our vets? Especially when you can read about them in books and watch them on television. 'The James Herriot factor was certainly very influential when I was at university', admits Grizelda Williams. 'And today it's programmes on the television like *Animal Hospital*. I suppose we'll soon be able to blame Rolf Harris for inspiring a whole new generation of vets!'

So you want to be a vet

IT IS MID-MARCH and the first spring sunshine heralds the beginning of a weekend when the Bristol Veterinary School will open its doors to aspiring young vets. They are all sixth-form students and, although they are still a year away from sitting their A levels, they've travelled from all over the country to register an early interest in fighting for one of the coveted places on a veterinary degree course.

The school is looking at its best. It is clear enough to see the surrounding Mendip Hills and sufficiently warm to tempt a few people out on to the site in shirtsleeves. It may even be pleasant enough to tempt the parents who have accompanied their 17-year-olds to make use of the brochure they are handed on arrival. Produced by the local council, it promotes the delights of the nearby seaside resort of Weston-super-Mare. If they don't fancy a day at the seaside, they will have to find something else to do. There are 120 sixth-formers here today and not enough room for their parents.

The day is called 'VetQuest' and is designed to introduce prospective students to what is involved in a veterinary degree course. Along the way there'll be tips on how to maximise their chances of selection and a tour of the site, with the school's final-year students as guides.

During the morning session the nervous young students listen politely and unresponsively to a succession of eminent vets who, by and large, do not display a natural talent for public speaking. There is a barely audible titter when one of the speakers mentions the problem of 'getting an arm stuck up a cow's backside' and a slight murmur of disapproval when another warns that large-animal practice 'is a tough job for a girl – very physical'. Three-quarters of the final-year students at Langford are women, and most of them seem tough enough.

However, although it is all rather low key, the programme covers the territory with speeches from small-animal, farm-animal and equine vets, along with contributors from academia and industry. And the Head of the Veterinary School at Langford, Professor Philip Duffus, is a relaxed and convincing public speaker. He outlines the curriculum and entry qualifications in some detail.

The sixth-formers will need A-levels in Chemistry and Biology or Zoology and one other academic subject – preferably a science subject. The Chemistry is compulsory, and candidates offering an alternative science subject to Biology or Zoology are only considered in exceptional circumstances. GCSE qualifications are also important. The veterinary schools expect 'a wide spread with good grades'. If candidates do not offer A-level Physics and/or A-level Biology, they must have obtained good passes in these subjects at GCSE.

However, Professor Duffus stresses that qualifications alone are not enough. 'Motivation is a terribly important thing. You are not going to get into a veterinary school without motivation.' The Professor tells the young students that he expects a lot because 'the country is investing a lot in the future of people like yourselves'. It costs about £100,000 to train a vet, making it the most expensive university course in the country.

He goes on to explain that the curriculum is undergoing some radical changes, particularly in respect of the emphasis on more practical work during the fifth year. 'The reason is that until recently lecturers were just continuing to teach facts rather than principles. Students were memorising rather than studying and the way you were getting through exams was by going into autopilot and regurgitating what you saw on pages 1 to 20.'

Professor Duffus then takes his audience through the details of the course year by year. Most of the teaching during the first three years of study is done in Bristol, although during this period students also spend one day a week at Langford. The programme is taught at three main sites: the Veterinary Preclinical School and the School of Medical Sciences, both of which are within the main University complex in Bristol, and the Department of Clinical Veterinary Science at Langford, some 14 miles south of the city. In the fourth and final years students are based entirely at Langford and are taught clinical veterinary science

Langford boasts some of the most up-to-date facilities. Here, student Jonathan Wray checks the results of a cardiogram with Eithne Comerford and Paul Wotton.

in the environment of the teaching hospital and veterinary practice units.

There is a varied approach to teaching, which includes lectures, practicals, demonstrations, tutorials in small groups, projects undertaken on both a group and individual basis, and computer-aided learning. In addition there is something called 'directed self-education' (DSE), which requires students to research topics and present the results in an oral, written or computer-based format.

The aim of the preclinical study is to provide a firm, basic knowledge of the normal structure and function of the animal body. Students also undertake studies of disease and its treatment. Throughout this period they also study animal management, production and husbandry, with the emphasis on how these contribute to the health and welfare of animals.

During the first year the subjects studied are Anatomy, Animal Management, Biochemistry and Physiology. There are also 'short units' on welfare and ethics, veterinary first aid, learning and communication skills, and computing.

In the second year students complete their study of anatomy and physiology. At this time some of the 'paraclinical' subjects are introduced into the course, including parasitology, pharmacology and epidemiology.

The third year includes further study of the 'paraclinical' subjects, namely pathology, pharmacology, microbiology and immunology. There are also courses in clinical science, including anaesthesia, the principles of disease management and surgery, and pig and poultry husbandry.

Examinations are held in January and June. In addition, the directed self-education component is assessed throughout the year and the mark contributes to the end-of-year result.

The final two years are based at Langford, where students study reproduction, pathology, clinical science and public health. Most of the formal teaching during this period takes place in the fourth year, leaving the fifth relatively free of lectures so that students can concentrate on their clerking rotations. 'The final year only has three major subjects and might look quite easy!' says Professor Duffus. 'Well, it isn't. You should see some of our students the morning after a night-time clerking emergency to see how hard we push students in the final year. Sometimes you don't have time to shut your eyes.'

The examination system is a mixture of continuous assessment and written tests, which can be multiple-choice question papers, essays and short-answer papers and oral examinations. The final examination in the clinical subjects also includes a practical clinical assessment. On graduation, successful students are admitted to the Royal College of Veterinary Surgeons in a ceremony during which they 'solemnly declare that my constant endeavour will be to ensure the welfare of animals committed to my care'.

Most veterinary graduates go straight into general practice. Some go into research at universities or research institutes and an increasingly significant minority go into industry. It is partly because some students choose to pursue careers other than as practising vets that employment prospects are so good for the remainder. Unemployment certainly is not a problem, with today's graduates tending to specialise in particular areas of farm or companion-animal practice.

There is a lot of study and it is a long slog from ambitious sixth-former to qualified vet. But Professor Duffus is keen to stress that studying does not end when they sit their finals. 'When you qualify you have got 30 or 40 years of professional life in front of you. It's up to us to bring to you the desire to continue the learning process.'

The sixth-formers have now spent the whole morning sitting in what is rather grandly described as a 'conference room'. The session has undoubtedly been useful but could hardly be described as lively. They have been talked at – in semi-darkness so that an extensive sequence of overhead projections can be shown – and this has all contributed to what can only be described as a slightly soporific atmosphere.

All that is about to change. The organisers of VetQuest have had the novel and rather inspired idea of providing a tour of the school with fifth-year students as guides. It is now lunchtime, and the sixth formers are led downstairs to the canteen where they are introduced to Steve Leonard. The sunshine has obviously affected Steve. He arrives in a tatty rugby shirt, cut-off jeans and, on the end of his long bare legs, a pair of old training shoes. For their part the 'VetQuesters' – as they have been nicknamed – are washed and scrubbed and dressed in their best interview clothes. 'Remember,' says one apologetically, 'we had to travel here with our parents.'

The staff who are organising this unique day have been stressing that VetQuest is not designed simply to encourage students to apply for a place on a veterinary degree course, nor is it intended to promote Bristol's virtues over the other five veterinary schools. If the sixth-formers decide at the end of it that veterinary science is not for them, that in itself is part of the day's purpose. And, although VetQuest is a Bristol initiative, the dining-hall where they will all have lunch is, rather bizarrely, lined with television monitors extolling the virtues of the veterinary schools in London, Edinburgh, Cambridge, Liverpool and Dublin. It may be very egalitarian – but it also necessitates much raising of voices to get a conversation going.

Steve Leonard, a dizzy mixture of undiplomatic charm and bon-homie, immediately kicks the notion of even-handedness into touch by revealing that he has been asked to 'sell Bristol University and its good aspects'.

Then he's off on the Bristol Vet School tour with a dozen students in tow, all of them increasingly intrigued by their sartorially challenged guide. Steve walks fast and talks even faster. 'Have you been told how this course is broken up?' Not waiting for an answer he continues. 'You spend the first three years in Bristol and two years out here. And this is where it's really at, where you do all the clinical stuff and start doing things on animals rather than listening to lectures all day.'

First stop, the small-animal hospital. Steve displays a real pride in the fact that this building has been put up since he arrived at the University. His enthusiasm alone makes him a splendid advocate for Bristol. 'If your own vet can't work it out, they'll send your pet to the small-animal hospital. The students get to see the animal first for a consultation. Oh, and by the way, the SMA is the major feline research centre in the world. This is where cats are at basically!'

On to the large-animal practice which, to the delight of the sixth-formers, Steve introduces with a particularly undiplomatic sentence. 'The farmers get discounts for letting students come in and botch things up.' And there's more. 'We got a calf in which had managed to impale itself on a stake. Normally it would have been sent off for slaughter. Instead it comes in here so we can have a go and do some surgery.' A short pause to let the information sink in, and then the payoff line. 'And when we've finished it still dies, but at least we've done some surgery!'

It is all great knockabout stuff and the once-nervous, unresponsive students are convulsed with fits of laughter. Now they are really listening and involved, Steve reins back on the humour to commend Langford as 'the best veterinary school in the country'. He claims that at the other five vet schools there are far fewer opportunities for surgical practice, pointing out that 'here we get four or five weeks' spaying'.

The sixth-formers are now asking their first questions of the day. What's the course like? ... is it fun? 'The final year is the best', says Steve. 'You're basically acting as a vet under supervision.' Is he worried about exams? 'I'm more worried about after the exams. You suddenly think, shit, in a few months' time someone is going to be *paying* me to do this and there'll be no one looking over my shoulder offering advice.' What's the social life like? 'The vets here have a notorious reputation for drinking their way through their university years', reveals Steve – who is teetotal. 'I just remember everything and in the morning tell them what they did.'

They have now arrived at the equine diagnostic centre. It is here, Steve explains, that horses are treated for lameness, colic and heart conditions. 'We also get quite a lot of racehorses with respiratory problems. Are any of you horsy?' The response is a loud chorus of 'Yes!' 'Oh no,' groans Steve, 'that's terrible, really terrible.'

Steve Leonard is not fond of horses by any means and he doesn't mind who knows it. For one thing, he tells his now captivated audience, they are so antisocial about when they 'decide' to have a medical problem. 'It's a kind of out-of-hours sort of thing with horses', he explains. 'They don't get ill until about 11 o'clock at night. Then they don't decide to go surgical until two o'clock in the morning. Then, if you're very lucky, they die and you can go to bed.'

Steve describes horses as 'evil, bad-tempered creatures'. Interestingly, he appears to have inherited these feelings from his veterinarian father and brothers, who refuse to deal with them. However, at Bristol the next vet in the family – who by common consent displays a natural affinity and confidence with other animals – has had to learn to deal with the family's *bête noire*.

Steve tells a story about a late-night emergency when a vet – not one from the University – asked him to shave a horse's neck in preparation for a catheter so that they could anaesthetise it. 'The horse was being a bit of a git and started barging me and I thought, I'm not going to be able to do this, so I called the vet. He was very narked and when he came in he punched the horse in the mouth, kicked it in the belly a few times and then punched it in the mouth again. Eventually it just stood still.'

A number of sixth-form jaws drop as the story is recounted before Steve emphasises that this is not a textbook method for calming a horse. However, for him the moral of the story is the absolute necessity for a vet to exercise his or her dominance over the animal they are treating. 'Take dogs for example. If you don't exert dominance over your pet dog, that's when it starts biting your kids, it starts biting other people and you have problems. But if you actually show dominance it fits the dog into its hierarchy, it knows where it's supposed to be and it has a much happier life. It's kind of cruel to be kind, kind of thing.'

This has been a uniquely Steve Leonard kind of tour kind of thing. And, before it ends, he cannot resist one more wisecrack at the expense of his least favourite animal. 'If having weighed up all the options you really do feel the need to smack a horse in the mouth, I can offer one piece of advice. Make sure the owner isn't looking.'

Back at the canteen there is a buffet lunch waiting, along with five television monitors offering the official video version of life at the other veterinary schools. The lunch is welcome, but none of the sixth-formers shows the remotest interest in the promotional tapes broadcasting around the room. Perhaps it all seems a little dull and sanitised in comparison with their tour of a real, live veterinary centre. They settle down eagerly to eat with Steve. What has been the effect of his unofficial, occasionally undiplomatic tour of Langford?

'Have I put anybody off?' asks the guide.

The response is a loud chorus. 'No!'

'Oh, damn', laughs Steve.

'Holidays'

IT IS NOW APRIL, the eve of the Easter holidays. There is a palpable air of tension among the undergraduates at the Bristol Veterinary School as they prepare to return home for what should be their last vacation as a student. By the summer holidays most of them expect to be working as qualified vets. First, though, they have to pass their finals – and that is why all of them know that what lies immediately ahead will be no vacation. Their three-week Easter 'break' will consist of a stress-inducing combination of last-minute revision and assisting qualified vets near their parents' homes. What this means in practice is swotting for exams during the evening and rehearsing veterinary skills during the day.

Bristol is particularly proud of its vacation studies scheme – or 'foster practice', as it is known – which covers both farm and veterinary practice. Vacations in the first and second years concentrate on farm practice, while from the third year students spend a considerable amount of time observing and assisting practice with veterinary surgeons. The scheme is a statutory requirement at Bristol and, despite the extra pressures it inevitably brings, is enthusiastically supported by the students.

Equally crucial, though, is the support of the profession. The Head of the Veterinary School at Langford, Professor Philip Duffus, says that the British approach to training veterinary scientists is quite different from the way it's done in other parts of the world. What makes it unique is that the universities have always involved the profession as part of the teaching process. 'They don't charge us anything for offering our students foster-practice placements during the holidays. The idea of becoming a vet and putting your own bit back into the educational process over your lifetime in practice seems to come quite naturally to people. And, remember, those people probably benefited from a similar freebie practical education themselves.'

However, Professor Duffus is keen to stress that foster practice is not simply of benefit to the students. Qualified vets, he insists, look forward to opening their doors to fifth-year students because many of them have been exposed to ideas at the cutting edge of veterinary science during their time at university. 'Students will say, what about this approach, and maybe the practitioner hadn't heard of that particular approach and says, oh, right let's try it. They're very bright and they do challenge you intellectually and that can be very stimulating. They're so hungry for information and it's a pleasure to be in their company. They're fun.'

All Britain's veterinary schools encourage students to attach themselves to a practice during their holidays, but Professor Duffus believes the Bristol approach is different: 'We don't rely on the *ad hoc* approach which some of the other schools still do.' In other words, Bristol is proud of the control it exercises over its pupils' vacation schemes.

The students are not simply allowed to fix themselves up with any practice they like. The emphasis is on selecting a placement that will give them a wide range of experience. Left to their own devices, students may not make the right choice. Professor Duffus didn't. 'It actually went wrong for me when I was a student. I was so keen on working abroad and research that I never saw the depth of practice that I should have done. That was because it was left to me. There was no control over us.'

These days it seems it is impossible for veterinary students to escape the extraordinarily focused and full-time attention that is given to their education. There is no let-up, particularly at this time of year. 'It has always been tough, but it's about to get a lot tougher', warns Professor Duffus. But he also believes that is no bad thing. 'I often wonder if some of the veterinary students here almost need that sort of pressure to do well.'

Tonight, though, most of them have turned up for a 'social' with the expressed intention of forgetting the pressure, if only for a few hours. The term will end in traditional style with plenty of drink and lots of noise. The students bar is the venue for a one-off performance by the 'Langford Stranglers'. The band is a curious hybrid, consisting of greying, balding, overweight teachers and fresh-faced, earnest-looking students in sunglasses. As they tune up they face a barrage of good-natured insults. One of the women students in the audience shouts 'You look dreadful!' But she hasn't heard them play. When they begin their hour-long set of 'covers' from the fifties, sixties, seventies and eighties they are loud – very loud – and pretty dreadful.

Still, no one seems to mind. Everyone is determined to have a good time. This is their last opportunity to let their hair down before finals, and the whole place goes wild. Most of the students seem to have a drink in one hand and a cigarette in the other, though the teetotal, non-smoking, clean-living Steve Leonard seems to have no need of such stimulants. He appears to be waging a one-man campaign to reintroduce 'pogoing', the highly energetic and completely unrhythmic dance craze popularised during the punk era. Leaping up and down in the middle of the dance floor he has his eyes closed, lost in the music, drunk on the atmosphere and apparently oblivious to everyone around him.

This is pure escapism, a chance for just one evening to forget the pressures that lie ahead. And there are plenty of those – revision, foster practice, clerking, finals and job hunting. If any students have earned the right to forget it all for a few hours, this bunch has. It is a terrific night, revealing the real camaraderie that exists among the students and demonstrating that as well as knowing how to work and study they also know how to play and party.

The night after the Langford Stranglers' end-of-term performance student Julie Richards is back in another bar – but this one belongs to her parents. Julie has returned to her home in the Liverpool suburb of Gateacre. Her father, John, and mother, Norma, run 'The Bear and Staff', a popular pub and restaurant. Yesterday Julie was dancing the night away with her boyfriend. This evening she is waiting on tables in Mum and Dad's pub. The deal is simple, says John. 'She works here in the pub when she's home, otherwise she doesn't get fed!'

Julie is paid the same hourly rate as the rest of the staff. It helps provide her with a little extra cash and, in particular, some money to run her Ford Fiesta. A car is vital for students living out in Langford if they are not to become completely stranded and detached from life in Bristol.

It is a particularly busy evening in The Bear and Staff. A lot of customers have decamped here after the Aintree Grand National. Julie has swapped her usual white veterinary coat for a spotted waitress's dress. She has done this many times before during holidays and weekends and her friendly, easy-going nature is much in evidence as she serves dozens of meals with practised efficiency and good humour.

After closing time the Richards family sit down for a well-earned drink. Julie's parents are understandably and conspicuously proud of their daughter. All her examination certificates from GCSE onwards are framed and hung on the sitting-room wall. Father John, who was a lab technician at the nearby Ford car factory before he moved into pub and restaurant management 15 years ago, says he and his wife worked hard to give both their daughters a private education. 'We've always saved a lot for their education and have made sacrifices for both of the girls really. It was a bit of a financial shock when we realised Julie would be going to university for five years rather than three. I've told her the standing order stops as soon as she has passed her finals!'

It is a lighthearted threat which would be unlikely to bother Julie even if it was meant to be taken seriously. Finding a job will probably not be difficult for any of the newly qualified vets. Almost certainly, all of them will be earning a good salary with a company car and free housing – a typical package for a new vet – before the end of the summer. Already there are plenty of advertisements appearing in the trade press from veterinary practices desperate to attract the next set of graduates.

Julie's academic path from school pupil to university student has been a familiar one. She was always at or near the top of the class in most subjects. And, in common with most of her colleagues at the veterinary school, she showed a prodigious appetite for hard work from an early age. 'She has always studied incredibly hard', says her father. 'And it paid off. After her GCSEs she had done so well in all her subjects that her teachers said, "you've got a lovely dilemma". She could have done almost anything ... languages, law, it was all possible. But Julie herself decided she wanted to be a vet.'

The Richards' other daughter, Andrea, is two years younger. She never shone at school academically and left aged 16. Andrea has travelled to her parents' house for the weekend from her home on the Isle of Man, where she works for Barclays Bank. She too is proud of Julie's achievements but says she was more than a little surprised when her sister chose veterinary science as a profession. 'To be truthful I was amazed because when she was growing up I didn't see a particularly big interest in animals. But I think it was just a choice between a doctor and a vet, really, and she went for the vet option because it was more demanding.'

Andrea's observations about Julie's inspiration and motivation tend to reinforce the much-quoted view that bright children are attracted to veterinary science as a challenge rather than as a vocation. However, the James Herriot factor was obviously influential too. Julie was always drawn to the books and the BBC television series and gently scolds her family for implying that she was not interested in animals. 'I *do* like animals as well, you know. It really isn't just about choosing the most difficult course.'

The fact is, though, that she has chosen one of the most difficult courses, and the next few weeks are likely to be the toughest of the last five years. Julie must revise at every possible moment, along with carrying out her foster-practice duties. Her sister, Dad and Mum are clearly still amazed by Julie's capacity for hard work. 'A typical day begins at about 7 a.m.', says Norma. 'She gets up, goes for a half-hour jog and then studies until lunchtime. After lunch she revises for the rest of the afternoon. In the early evening she'll go for a swim. She'll then study until 10 o'clock, when she has her supper. Then it's off to bed and the same routine the following day.'

The Richards are a close-knit family and, when Julie headed south to the Bristol Veterinary School five years ago, it was clearly a wrench. Norma is reminding her family that after a month Julie rang her up to complain that she didn't like it. 'I said you've got to give it twelve months. If you still don't like it after a year, then you can come home.'

Julie does remember that phone call. It was a difficult time, she recalls. 'I was quite lonely. I knew I had been top of the class at school, but at vet school everyone has got straight As and you begin to think, maybe I'm not good enough.' 'You were also a bit daunted by the backgrounds of some of the other students', her Father recalls. 'Yes,

I suppose I was', agrees Julie. 'A lot of them have got a veterinary history or come from farming backgrounds. But it wasn't that long before I realised that I was good enough to be there. I finally realised I wasn't lonely when I forgot Dad's birthday!'

Julie has rarely been homesick since, though she does return to the family home regularly. Her bedroom is pretty much how she left it when she was 18. On the door is a car number plate which reads 'VET 1'; inside it is very pink, with a large collection of teddy bears. This is where she shuts herself away for up to 14 hours a day to do her revision.

At this stage in the course Julie, like all the students, can see an end in sight to five years' hard slog. The dream that many of them have had since childhood of becoming a vet is tantalisingly close to becoming a reality. Professor Philip Duffus says that all students who have made it this far are capable of passing their finals and qualifying as vets. But he adds a caveat. 'They are going to have to continue working as hard as they can right up to their exams. Some of those who fail do so because they take too much for granted.'

However, at this stage relaxing and taking things for granted is not the biggest threat to success. Professor Duffus says the time spent contemplating exams over the Easter break is not simply a case of plenty of revision. Finals are as much an emotional and psychological challenge as an intellectual one. 'The majority of them actually fail because of nerves – they get panicky. If you are around the vet school during finals you'll see people who you felt were outgoing and happy looking awful. You only have to look at them to see how much stress they're under. Once they get to that stage it's almost a relief to put an exam paper in front of them. At least then they can concentrate on the business in hand rather than simply worrying about it.'

At this stage, eight weeks before her finals, Julie Richards appears calm, focused and ready for the challenge that lies ahead. It is late in the evening and a single desk light illuminates her revision notes. The desk is tidy and uncluttered. She is transcribing notes from a textbook on to sheets of A4 paper. Julie works in a systematic, organised fashion. It is her way of ensuring that she does not panic as exams approach. During the finals fifth-year students are examined in three subjects: surgery, medicine and public health. So she splits her revision

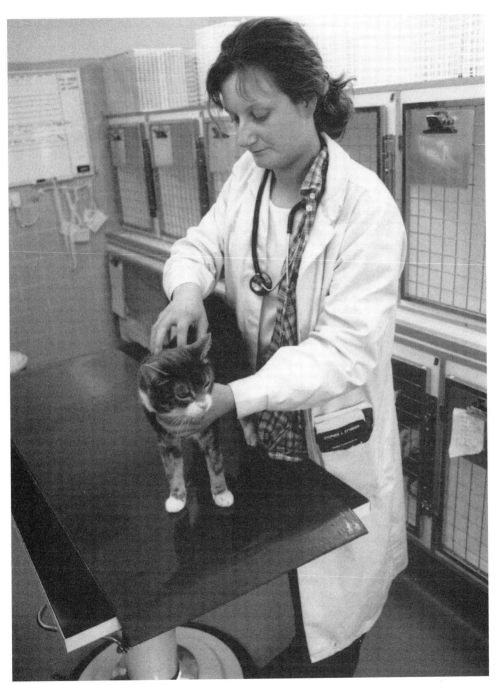

Julie Richards with a diabetic cat.

day into three parts – surgery in the morning, medicine in the afternoon and public health, her biggest concern, in the evening.

Julie is confident of passing but is not taking anything for granted. 'There's so much to learn, but when I need reassurance that I will pass I remind myself I have not failed an exam since I've been to university. But it isn't easy. I do have to spend a lot of time revising because I do find it difficult to learn things.'

The next morning Julie is up early for her first stint of foster practice during these Easter holidays. It is a half-hour car journey from her home in Liverpool to the Rose Cottage veterinary practice in Frodsham in Cheshire. Julie has worked here during university holidays for the last two years. Today she is assisting and observing veterinary surgeon Ken Robinson.

It is a mixed and very large practice, so there is plenty of variety. The day begins with a very sick-looking grey cat that is panting hard and clearly in some distress. He has been a problem patient for some time, explains Ken. 'He was presented a few weeks ago with anorexia. After a clinical examination we found a swollen thyroid gland in his neck. But we now discover he has an abdominal pain as well, so it's possible there are two quite separate things wrong.'

Ken Robinson decides to perform an exploratory operation to examine the cat's internal organs, particularly the liver. He is worried it could be cancer. This is specialist work and Julie will not be invited to assist, only to look on as Ken removes a number of samples. They will be sent to Pathology, and it will be several days before the results are known.

Once the operation is complete Julie quickly slips out of her surgical gown for some more routine consultations. However, plenty of the so-called routine work is anything but routine for a student who is being confronted with many animals for the first time. Mr and Mrs Williams walk into surgery with their blue budgie and announce: 'He's off colour'. How can they tell? A different shade of blue perhaps?

Fortunately there are some more obvious and telltale signs. He is also off his food and vomiting. 'Does he mind being handled?' asks Ken as he reaches inside the cage to examine the budgie. No need for the Williams to reply, for as soon as the vet gets his hand round the bird it begins to make a pitiful and distressed high-pitched screeching noise. Once it is calmer, Ken gently puts a stethoscope to its chest and shows Julie, who has been standing well back, how to hold a budgie for examination. Basically, the technique involves turning the bird on its back and gripping it firmly in one hand. It is a relatively simple procedure but one that could prove embarrassing for a newly qualified vet who has not had the chance to practise it.

Like most of the students, Julie laments the rather limited amount of time the vet school is able to devote to teaching related to 'exotic' animals. Now, though, at least she will be properly prepared when she has to handle her first budgie in practice. Ken Robinson reckons this one probably has a kidney infection. He prescribes antibiotics administered by an injection.

Ken handles the clients and their pets with a friendly, easy and rapid efficiency. There are plenty more waiting outside and, as in any business, time is money. As soon as Mr and Mrs Williams have left with their off-colour blue budgie, Julie calls in the next customer. Paul Gregson has a rather unusual pet under his arm. 'Iggy' is an anorexic iguana.

Julie is obviously charmed by this friendly, prehistoric-looking reptile. 'Ah, isn't he sweet', she says, stroking Iggy's neck. 'How old is he?' 'About two years old I think', says Mr Gregson. 'They live to thirty, you know, and they're really good companions.' 'Does he like everybody?' asks Julie. 'Well, he really likes me. But, to be honest, he's not so keen on the wife and kids. They get on better with our two dogs and four cats.'

Iggy has been to the Rose Cottage surgery before. He is undergoing a course of antibiotic injections which, his owner says, have really perked him up. However, although the treatment may be working, the iguana is not keen on the needle. He seems to sense what is coming next as soon as he is put on the consultation table. There is a brief and bizarre struggle as two vets in white coats and an owner in a denim jacket try to restrain a large iguana and wrap him in a bath towel. Once the task is complete Iggy can wriggle no more; in a few seconds he has had the injection and is soon back in Mr Gregson's arms behaving in a perfectly relaxed manner.

When Iggy and his owner have left the consulting room Julie talks to Ken about her concerns – the gaps in her knowledge. 'I really like reptiles, but I wouldn't want to specialise in them because I know so little about them at the moment. It's awful, really, because we get loads and loads of lectures on dogs and cats and we get like 20 minutes on reptiles.'

Ken Robinson is sympathetic. He knows that veterinary teaching concentrates on dogs and cats. It has to, for those are the animals that vets in a mixed practice will spend most of their time treating. However, he does feel that some animals are neglected, though he's not referring to iguanas or even budgies. 'I'm talking about rabbits. Do you know that they are the third most common animals we see?' 'Yes,' says Julie, 'and we've only had one lecture on rabbits.'

She doesn't say how many lectures they've had on the next creature that comes in for examination. 'Charlie Finnegan' is a rather sick-looking nine-year-old cockatoo. When the owner explains his recent medical history it is easy to appreciate why he's not feeling so happy about life. Two weeks ago he had a tumour removed from his groin – and then promptly developed a feather disorder which has left him with a very bare chest. Now poor old Charlie Finnegan has become anorexic as well.

It is a familiar condition at this morning's surgery and the treatment is equally familiar – an injection of antibiotic. Like Iggy the iguana, Charlie the cockatoo is a friendly, easy-going sort of animal until he goes anywhere near a vet's consulting table and, in particular, anywhere near a needle. There have been signs of growing tension ever since he first appeared in the room tucked inside his owner's coat. She has been trying to coax a few words from him – 'Charlie is normally very chatty', she says. Silence. The cockatoo is clearly devoted to his owner and nuzzles against her neck. But as she attempts to remove him from her coat and pass him to the vet, Charlie Finnegan – encouraged to 'keep his pecker up' – suddenly gets his pecker out and directs it at lightning speed towards his owner's hand. She lets out a yelp of pain as the peck draws blood. Not surprisingly, Charlie then gets the towel treatment before his injection. 'He's a lot brighter than he was', remarks his owner as she leaves the surgery nursing a sore hand.

After a morning of 'exotics', it must be something of a relief for Julie to begin the afternoon with a dog. Becky is a King Charles Spaniel. She is having real problems giving birth, probably because

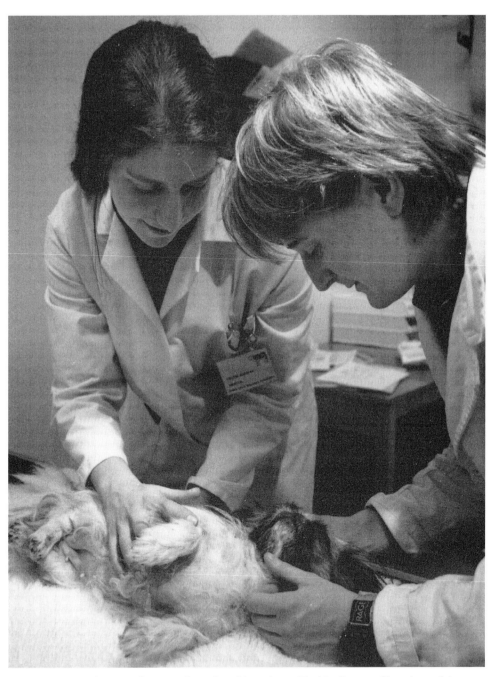

Not as exotic as a cockatoo, perhaps, but this patient with skin disease still needs careful handling – as students Louise Norman and Phillipa Hughes discover.

she's still very young. Becky is only seven months old and has become pregnant in her first season. Her present owners haven't had her long and Ken suspects she was already pregnant when they bought her.

Becky really shouldn't be breeding until her third season. Her owners had no idea she was pregnant until 'a pup dropped out while she was playing with our ten-year-old son'. Since then two other puppies have been successfully delivered. But Becky has shown no interest in her offspring, and all of them are now having to be bottle-fed by Julie and the nursing staff. Even more worrying is the fact that there is still one more pup to be delivered, but the young King Charles Spaniel, barely out of puppyhood herself, is showing no interest in getting on with the job. This could be dangerous for both young mum and unborn pup. So Julie is soon back in the operating theatre for the second time that day, this time watching and assisting Ken Robinson with a caesarean.

When the fourth pup, the only boy, is delivered he is struggling to survive. Julie is given the job of trying to revive him and begins to rub the back of his neck, a little tentatively at first. 'You need to be a bit more rough with him', advises Ken. Julie rubs more vigorously and, after a few minutes, the tiny creature lets out a few little squeaks. This is the cue for Ken to place a tube in the puppy's mouth and blow some pure oxygen into his lungs. 'The atmosphere only contains a small proportion of oxygen', he explains to Julie. 'This pure stuff should help his breathing.' 'Is he going to survive now, do you think?' she asks. 'Yes, I think he will', says Ken, '… the real danger period has passed.'

It has been a long day for Julie Richards. It is nearly 10 p.m. when she finishes and there is no prospect of doing any revision this evening. She now has another appointment, part professional, part social. Julie has been invited to dinner with Bill and Chris Henry, the owners of the Rose Cottage practice. Bill is a vet and wife Chris is the practice manager. They set up the business 12 years ago and since then it has expanded rapidly. It is now modern and well-equipped and employs seven vets and five veterinary nurses. 'It's been a busy day today', Julie tells the Henrys as she tucks into the curry they have prepared for her. 'I've done loads. It's been very eventful. Sorry I'm late, but we had a caesarean right at the end of the day.'

For Julie even this meal is part of her education. She is hungry for information. Now she is just a few months away from being a qualified vet she wants to know what it will be like. Chris Henry says that many of the students are in for a surprise. 'It's a real shock to discover that the profession you've chosen is really a service industry. You have to offer the clients a really good level of service, otherwise they won't come back. And people make constant demands on you.'

Julie thinks her family background might help. 'The Richards may not be vets, but all of us certainly know what it's like to work in a service industry. I'm used to dealing with the public when I waitress or work behind the bar – and I certainly know how awkward they can be on occasions.'

The Henrys tell Julie that the ability to talk to clients is a key skill for any vet and one which can sometimes be difficult to acquire in the rarefied academic world of an elite university course. But foster practice does give students a chance to polish up their communication skills.

'Veterinary students are always very academic,' observes Chris, 'and to explain to owners simply what is wrong with their animals isn't easy for some people.' Husband Bill, a vet for 24 years, agrees. 'I have a very basic saying, which I often repeat: "It doesn't take two As and a B to be a veterinary surgeon". It worries me that we're still clamouring for those high academic standards – and I fear we lose some potentially very good vets along the way.'

Julie wants some tips about securing a job. 'What sort of questions do you ask newly qualified vets when they come for interview?' The Henrys say there are no set questions but that everybody interviewed will spend a full day in the practice and must demonstrate an ability to get on with everybody – vets, nurses and clients.

As the conversation continues it becomes clear that the Henrys see the issue of job hunting from a very different perspective. They have been around long enough to know that it is employers rather than potential employees who face the major problem. Newly qualified vets may have to compete to work in a particularly favoured practice, but none of them is going to have any problem finding work. However, plenty of practices have enormous difficulty finding new vets.

Last year the Henrys spent a thousand pounds putting an advertisement in the trade magazine, *The Veterinary Record*. 'That's a very big investment', Chris tells Julie. 'And a big risk too. Luckily it paid off and we had six applications.' Six may not sound a lot, but it is considerably above average. Indeed, some practices get no response at all.

'With the current shortage of vets you've got to advertise yourself', says Bill. 'It's a bit like selling a house. Once you get them across the door, show them the kitchen, show them the bathroom, you've got a good chance of doing a deal. Similarly, once we get them into Rose Cottage they usually want to work for us.' It certainly worked last year. The Henrys' advertisement bagged them the top student from Liverpool Veterinary School.

This is all reassuring news for Julie. However, to become the sought-after commodity that new vets clearly are, she first has to pass her finals. Bill and Chris can only sympathise when the anxious student talks about the pressures of the final year. 'There's so much revision that many of the fifth-year students go through phases where they think, I just don't want to be a vet any more. I've thought it myself.'

After dinner Julie returns to the surgery. By now it is midnight, but the student wants to witness a happy conclusion to the emergency caesarean at which she assisted earlier. Julie is there to greet Becky's owners when they come in to collect their spaniel and her four puppies. The pups are now feeding from their mum and all appear to be doing well – even the small male which Julie had to revive. 'What are you going to call them?' asks Julie. 'We've got as far as Wallace and Gromit', says the ten-year-old boy, who saw the first birth at the beginning of the day. 'We were only expecting two, so we haven't made up our minds about other names.'

Julie Richards' housemate at vet school, Steve Leonard, has returned to his family home in Burley Dam in Cheshire for the Easter holidays. The Leonards are a remarkable veterinary family. Steve's father is a vet and so are his two elder brothers. Steve's younger brother is also training to be a vet at Liverpool University.

The 'boys', as their mother, Bet, refers affectionately to them, all display the same mixture of easy charm, humour and self-confidence. Bet has obviously been, and indeed continues to be, a huge influence on their lives. 'Mum's brilliant at helping us deal with the stress', says

Steve. 'Whenever I worry about exams she's always there to offer support and encouragement. Many is the time I've kept her up talking to the early hours of the morning when I've been worried. She's brilliant.'

For Steve the pressure now building as he approaches his finals is unfamiliar, slightly intimidating territory. But Bet has seen it all before. She has already shepherded Dennis and Tom through their finals and, after Steve, will have to do the same for her youngest, Keith. 'I'm totally there for them when they're stressed out. Being a mum, that's part of my job.'

Only part of her job, though. Bet is also a teacher, having got a degree in psychology after the four boys were born. She says she came from a family where it was considered that girls didn't need educating. 'If things had been different, who knows, I might have been a vet as well. I wish I'd had the chance really. It's outdoors, it's meeting people. It's an excellent job.'

Her admiring son readily agrees that Mum could have been a vet and endorses her view of the profession. 'It's the best job in the world. The only job that compares to it is being a medic. But the downfall of medics is that they have to specialise, so they don't get to do surgery and medicine. The other thing of course is that medics have to work inside hospitals – which smell!'

At this point mother and son fall about laughing. Their relationship is relaxed and close. Steve clearly adores his mother and being with her at home with finals only a matter of weeks away is obviously a source of great comfort. She reassures him that he has already done the really difficult bit – getting on the course. 'The A levels were the hardest. It's tough making the grades to get accepted for veterinary science. That was a really stressful time for me too, and with my boys it was like me doing A levels four times over.'

Steve is fairly relaxed about his finals but knows only too well that he has to guard against complacency. At the end of the first year he had to abandon a trip to the United States when he failed three of his exams. 'It was a bit of a nightmare', he recalls. 'But I passed the retakes with relative ease because I worked, basically. There's no question of me not working hard enough for my finals. I haven't come this far only to fall at the final hurdle.'

At his home in Nottingham finals are also occupying the thoughts of Jon Coupe. 'I can't think of anything else, basically. The pressure is enormous.' Alongside the sheer quantity of revision he must get through during these holidays, Jon feels the additional pressure of wanting to stop being a drain on his parents' financial resources. He knows that if he fails in July he will not be able to resit until September. After a five-year degree course most parents will be looking forward to their offspring earning a living as soon as possible. Jon is keen to begin repaying the investment sooner rather than later. 'I'm eternally grateful to my parents for funding what has been a long education. At times it's been a struggle for them to scrape the money together. I know they've made enormous sacrifices.'

Jon is also beginning to think beyond his finals and to the beginning of a career which is sure to create pressures of its own. Many students before him have come to recognise that earning the qualification is tough, but doing the job – particularly in the first year – is tougher still. So, just beyond all the tension surrounding exams is the prospect of something even more daunting – doing the job. 'When you start, it's a continual learning process' says Jon. 'After qualifying from the University you should be very good theoretically, but when you get out into practice it is a very different world.'

For several years now during his holidays Jon has been getting a taste of that world in a city-centre veterinary practice in Nottingham. John Davison, who is supervising him during the Easter break, agrees that the first year as a vet is particularly demanding. However, he has reassuring words for Jon. 'I think he has the personality and the knowledge to make the grade. He's really become quite an asset to this practice. He seems to be able to relate to all sorts of clients coming through the door and has a natural ability to deal with the surgical side.'

Jon Coupe will spend the remainder of his Easter holidays at the East Midlands practice of Davison and Davison. Across in the West Midlands Fiona Green has returned to her parents' house in Litchfield in Staffordshire for her Easter 'holiday'. Around the dinner table Mum, Dad and daughter are engaging in some good-natured banter about the colour of Fiona's hair. Rather unusually, she has dyed it brown although she is a natural blonde. Fiona's mother, Sandra, is convinced the change was provoked by a desire to be taken more seriously. 'She didn't want to be regarded as a dumb blonde.'

'Absolute rubbish', retorts Fiona. 'I once dyed my hair green as well. Now it's brown. I just do it for a change.'

But her mother persists. 'You were worried that farmers might not take you seriously.'

'I don't think the colour of my hair is going to make any difference.'

'I don't know. You're very small and slight. Some of my friends have said that you don't look strong enough to be a vet. They say "She doesn't look big enough". Women have only been accepted as vets quite recently.'

Fiona agrees that the increasing prevalence of women vets is a relatively recent phenomenon. She concedes, too, that professional women are sometimes judged by their appearance. But she will not accept that any of this was behind her decision to swap blonde for brunette. 'I still stand by the fact that I don't think my hair colour is going to make any difference as to whether farmers or any other clients are going to take me seriously.'

Fiona's father, Graham, is inclined to agree with his daughter and disinclined to continue the conversation about her hair colour. 'Oh come on, this isn't really an issue is it?' It is certainly difficult to imagine anyone refusing to take Fiona seriously for very long. She appears to be composed, articulate, mature and ferociously intelligent.

Graham Green is a scrap-metal dealer who runs his own business. It is clear that the parents have had to work hard to finance their daughter's unusually lengthy period of education. Fiona is now 26, and the veterinary course is her second degree. She already has a first in physiology from Oxford. Graham acknowledges that they have faced financial pressures, but is anxious to make light of them. 'I don't think we've ever really gone without anything we've really wanted.' 'No, I haven't been aware of anything,' agrees Sandra, 'but I suppose we will notice a difference in a positive sense when she finishes her education.' 'Yes, I will be quite glad when she starts to earn a living', laughs Graham.

Like many of the Bristol students, Fiona received her pre-university education in a fee-paying school. Her parents have been aware of her veterinary ambitions for a long time. 'She first decided she wanted to be a vet in her early teens', remembers Graham. 'I don't think we took it too seriously at first because a lot of children were interested in it at the time because of the Herriot books and television programmes. But she kept it up.'

Sandra recalls her daughter being motivated, determined and interested in animals from a young age. 'She was very definite about it from the age of fourteen. Fiona was always caring and wanted to help animals, but without being sentimental about it. I remember saying once "Why don't you think about being a doctor?" and she said "No, I don't want to treat human beings". And that was it.'

Sandra Green has many hopes invested in her daughter's future. She is proud of her Fiona's academic achievements but worries about the level of commitment that will be demanded in her chosen career. She wants her to be a successful vet and marry and have a family. 'You'll need to find a husband who will understand a job which can make a call on you 24 hours a day seven days a week.'

Later, revising in her study, Fiona talks about the pressures of being the only surviving child. Her brother, Paul, was killed in a car crash when she was sixteen. Since then Fiona's mother has worked unpaid for organisations that offer help to families who have faced similar bereavements. But the Greens' personal loss inevitably continues to affect their own family life a decade after the tragedy. 'Paul has been gone ten years. I feel like an only child and that somehow all my parents' hopes and expectations are now focused on me', says Fiona. 'Me and Paul were just beginning to become really good friends when he was killed.' His photo sits prominently on her desk.

The study is Fiona's retreat and has been ever since her parents converted it from an old bathroom when she began revising for her GCSEs. It still has many of her old secondary-school textbooks. 'You can see the development of my academic life in this room. It's my haven. There is nothing to disturb my concentration. I can't hear the stereo or TV but I can look through the window into the garden. It's very special.'

The books she will revise from for her finals are piled several feet high on her desk. 'When I first looked at them together like that it hit me just how much I've got to learn. I just thought to myself, oh my God.'

Daunted she may have been, but defeated, never. Like all the veterinary students, Fiona has the ability to work extraordinary hours to get on top of a subject. Even so, this is the first time she has found it necessary to begin revising for summer exams at Easter. She is already impressively well organised. Alongside the towering pile of textbooks is a neat handwritten timetable with details of exam dates and a revision schedule.

Like several of the students, Fiona believes that it is getting harder to learn things. She freely admits that it is difficult to keep the motivation going, particularly as this is her second degree. It is now eight years since she began her further education. 'Just now it seems like a very, very long time', she says ruefully.

Ideally, when she revises she likes to write down the main points. It helps them stick in her mind. However, for her veterinary finals there is simply too much information to do that. She would never get through it all. Fiona must content herself with highlighting important pieces of text and then reciting them out loud. 'I dread that feeling of turning an exam paper over and thinking, oh my god, I haven't revised this. The thought of having to revise over the summer for a resit fills me with horror. I'm determined to work hard enough to ensure that doesn't happen.'

Fiona is keen to stress that a young lifetime of academic achievement also represents a record of really hard work. She believes that other people, even those closest to her, do not appreciate that there is no gain without pain. 'Mum and Dad always assume that I'm going to be fine. "Oh, Fiona will be all right", they tell our family and friends. And that always puts extra pressure on me. I suppose that my academic record so far suggests they are right, but sometimes I don't think they understand how much work I have to do just so that they can sit back and assume I'll be all right.'

The following morning Fiona arrives early at the Pool House Veterinary Hospital, a turn-of-the-century red-bricked building in the centre of the cathedral city of Litchfield. She is a familiar figure here now, having spent several weeks at the practice during each of her holidays for the last three years.

Fiona will be working with vet Dougie Fountain, an amiable young Scotsman not much older than herself. Their first patient on the first morning of Fiona's last foster practice will prove to be one of the most tricky, tense and heart-rending small-animal cases she has ever had to deal with.

He is a friendly but sick-looking eight-month-old puppy called Charlie. A particularly appealing-looking German Shepherd cross, he has been brought back to the veterinary hospital by his owner, a young woman called Lisa Mason. It is Monday morning and, in fact, Charlie spent part of the weekend in the hospital after being admitted as an emergency case suffering from vomiting and diarrhoea.

Before asking Charlie and Lisa into the consulting room, Dougie Fountain outlines the situation to Fiona. 'The pup actually spent the weekend in the isolation ward because he's not vaccinated and we were a bit worried that he might be suffering from the parvovirus. But we gave him some drugs, put him on a special diet and he perked up. Didn't vomit or have diarrhoea all weekend. So we sent him home, but as soon as he got there it started all over again.'

Dougie wants Fiona to conduct the initial clinical examination on her own, so he nips off to attend to another client while the student invites Lisa and Charlie into the consulting room. Charlie looks like a very sick puppy indeed and Lisa Mason is clearly a very worried owner. Fiona is confident and sympathetic, a reassuring combination. She gently but firmly lifts Charlie on to the consultation table. 'You must be getting used to this place, Charlie. You've already been here for a weekend break.'

Lisa explains that Charlie had begun to vomit again in the night. 'He's not interested in food at all. Every time he is fed he is sick within minutes. It's been going on for a week now.' Charlie's appetite for food, and indeed life, has waned dramatically during those seven days. The normally boisterous, healthy puppy is now listless and conspicuously thin.

Fiona decides to investigate the possibility of a 'foreign body'. 'You haven't seen him eat anything he shouldn't, like a ball or something like that?'

'No, I haven't seen him swallow anything. But I have to say he normally chews everything up. I'm always having to take things out of his mouth.'

'Any chance he's eaten a bone or something like that?'

'No, we don't give him bones. He prefers socks and anything else from my underwear drawer.'

Fiona begins her examination by running her hands underneath Charlie's abdomen. It is obviously empty and tender. At one point the puppy, who has his head cradled in his owner's chest, turns momentarily to snap at the student vet. She appears unperturbed. 'It's all right sweetheart, I know it's sore.'

While Fiona takes Charlie's temperature, his owner talks with obvious affection about the puppy. 'I've had him since he was ten weeks old. He's very mischievous, always dragging clothes out of my wardrobe. That's why I called him Charlie – because he is so cheeky. It's a shame to see him the way he is because he's normally so energetic. I'm desperately worried he is going to have to be put down.'

The puppy's temperature is normal. Fiona excuses herself and goes to fetch Dougie. When they return the vet explains the diagnosis to Lisa. 'It could be one of two things: parvovirus because he hasn't had his injections or, more likely, he's swallowed something which he can't pass out.'

It is clear that Charlie is now a dangerously ill puppy and that he has deteriorated even since the weekend. He is becoming dehydrated, his coat is dull and his eyes are beginning to look distressingly sunken. The vets will have to act quickly as any delay now could jeopardise Charlie's chances of survival. Dougie tells the owner that there are two immediate priorities – to put the puppy on a drip to combat the dehydration and to try to establish whether the puppy's tummy does actually contain some foreign body. They will begin by taking an X-ray of his abdomen, but there is no guarantee that this will identify the problem. 'If it doesn't,' says Dougie, 'we should do an exploratory operation.'

This is distressing news for Lisa Mason, who is now on the verge of tears. Not only is it confirmation that Charlie is critically ill but it also raises the question of cost. Operations are expensive and Lisa, a part-time healthcare assistant who looks after children with learning disabilities, earns very little. She is worried that even if the vets have the skills to save her much-loved puppy, she may not have the cash.

Dougie Fountain tells her not to worry just yet. Perhaps the X-ray will reveal a problem that can be treated without surgery. Lisa

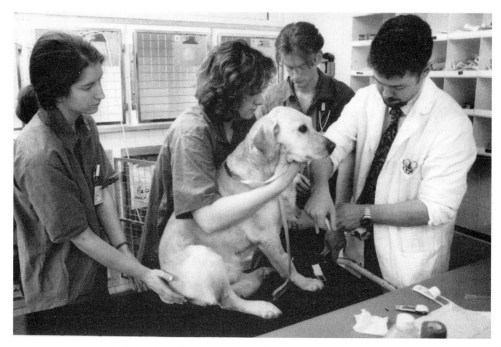

Difficult decisions. Jon Coupe with a labrador whose immune system is attacking its own white blood cells.

manages a half-hearted smile, grateful for some reassurance, but is probably beginning to recognise that difficult decisions may lie ahead. This is an uncomfortable time too for Fiona, who, because it is part of her training, must watch an owner in an emotionally distressed state. But although she has to look on, she cannot really help at this stage. At times like this the qualified vet must take control of the situation.

Lisa tells Dougie and Fiona that she will go to her parents' house and wait for a phone call there. Charlie is taken for his X-ray as soon as she has left. 'Oh dear, what a thin dog', remarks Fiona as she studies the results with Dougie. However, apart from accentuating the obvious fact that he has lost a great deal of weight, the X-ray does not provide conclusive evidence of the cause. 'He's a very sick dog, but there's nothing obvious which says there is a definite foreign body in there', concludes Dougie.

The vet and the student then begin a fairly lengthy debate about what to do next. To operate or not to operate, that is the question. And there is no simple answer. Surgery carries risks in any case, and in this case there is the added complication of the owner's financial situation combined with real uncertainty about whether an operation will find anything. On balance, though, if the money can be found, Dougie feels that an operation is the best way forward. 'If there is a foreign body in there it could cause a lot of damage – irreparable damage if it's left too long. You're better off opening them up unnecessarily than taking the risk of leaving it.'

However, Charlie cannot be taken to theatre just yet. Lisa will have to be telephoned and the puppy's condition will have to be stabilised. To do that they must deal with his dehydration straightaway. So Fiona carries a rather forlorn and bewildered young dog to the kennel, where a drip and a bandage are attached to his leg. He is then locked up in a small cage to await the outcome of the decisions that must be made over the coming hours.

Meanwhile Dougie Fountain is trying to contact Lisa by telephone. She isn't there, so he speaks instead to her mother. 'Charlie's condition is deteriorating and he has a very tender abdomen. Your daughter mentioned that he liked chewing things like her socks and I'm really quite concerned he may have swallowed something. I think we'll have to open him up.'

The response from the other end of the phone is predictable and understandable. 'The point is we're quite worried about money. My husband and I are pensioners and Lisa only has a part-time job. That's a problem. The treatment she's paid for already has absolutely broken her. She often goes without food herself so that she can feed the dog. So I'm just wondering what the cost will be if we give the go-ahead to operate.'

'You're probably talking about at least £200.'

'She just can't afford that. She's not here at the moment, but when she comes back she may decide that Charlie has to be put to sleep.'

'Ok, I understand', says Dougie. 'Please could you get her to ring me when she comes in. Or, if she prefers, she could pop over.'

'All right, I'll tell her the situation.'

Within an hour Lisa Mason has arrived back at the Pool House Veterinary Hospital. This time she is accompanied by a friend, and Fiona collects them from reception. She dispenses instant coffee and sympathy. It is obvious that Lisa has been crying and is aware that the life or death decision she must make is probably imminent. 'We really need to operate', says Fiona. Dougie is anxious to reassure Charlie's owner that no shame or stigma should be attached to her money worries. 'The financial aspects are something we come up against all the time. You've been very unlucky. You don't expect to collect a puppy and then just a few months later be landed with a two- or three-hundred pound bill.'

The veterinary costs are explained. It isn't simply a question of the surgery. There are the drugs and fluids, and up to four days of aftercare following the operation. If Lisa can finance the surgery there is a good prospect of Charlie making a full recovery, but no guarantee. She has to weigh up all the factors in the next few minutes. Dougie Fountain asks her whether it would help if the practice allowed her to pay the bill on a weekly or monthly basis. She shakes her head sadly.

'Thank you, but I just don't think I could raise the kind of money I think you need. How much is the operation?'

'About two hundred pounds. Is there any way you can afford it?'

'I just can't', sobs Lisa.

It is a heartbreaking moment. Fiona, who is clearly distressed too, can only look on as Lisa weeps quietly with her head in her hands and Dougie tries to offer sympathy. 'I'm so sorry. It's a horrendous situation to be in and a horrendous decision to make too.'

Putting Charlie to sleep appears to be an increasingly likely option. There is, however, one other – a treatment that may amount to little more than a stay of execution but could at least buy the distressed owner some time at relatively little cost. If they were to administer liquid paraffin for a couple of days it could lubricate Charlie's intestine and bowel sufficiently for him to be able to pass out the foreign body. However, if the puppy has swallowed a large object it is unlikely to work and the wait will increase the chances of whatever it is inside him ripping and irreparably damaging vital internal organs.

Dougie and Fiona decide to leave Lisa and her friend alone for ten minutes to consider the decision that has to be made. In another room, vet and student talk about a deeply affecting case. For Fiona in particular it has been an emotional morning – the kind of really raw experience that the veterinary school could not hope to prepare her for. You have to see it and live it to understand it. 'At Langford we don't get a great deal of teaching about how to deal with an owner when their animal has to be put down. I think we've had one seminar on it basically. But I'm not sure it's something you can teach someone anyway.'

Dougie doesn't think so either. 'It's just such an upsetting thing because you've got a lovely pup there. But as soon as you get into practice you're faced with this sort of thing all the time. I really feel bad saying we can't do the operation unless you pay for it. On the other hand, the business would collapse in no time at all if you kept saying we'll do this one for free because you feel sorry for them. All the same, it is heartbreaking.'

Fiona agrees. 'I actually felt quite close to tears myself when Charlie's owner was crying. I don't think there's anything wrong with a vet showing emotion, though, because it shows that you care for the animal and the client.'

It is time to return to Lisa Mason. She is a little more composed now, but the first thing she presents to Dougie and Fiona is not a decision but a request. 'Is it all right if I see him?' 'Of course', says the vet, and Fiona is dispatched to fetch Charlie. She brings him back, still attached to his drip. It makes for an odd and distressing sight – a puppy with no energy and no interest just lying limply in Fiona's arms. When he sees Lisa, though, he manages a brief wag of his tail. 'Hello, my baby', she cries, throwing her arms around him and bursting into tears once more. Between stifled sobs she whispers in his ear again and again: 'What have you been eating, my baby?' Then, turning to Fiona, she says, 'Let's give him a couple of days on the paraffin.' 'You can pop in any time you like', says Doug – an invitation that prompts a smile and even a joke: 'Can I sleep here with him please?'

As Lisa turns towards the door to leave, a very sick puppy summons what little energy he has left to try and climb into her arms. 'No Charlie, you can't come home just yet. Oh, you look so sorry for yourself, but you've got to stay here and get better.' 'If he passes anything out of his backside, the first thing we'll do is call you', says Doug. 'He's such a young dog that I really don't want to put him to sleep without at least giving him a chance.'

In fact, Doug Fountain is not optimistic about the liquid paraffin treatment dislodging whatever it is Charlie has inside him. Given Lisa's financial problems, though, he reckons it's worth a try. But without the cash necessary for the operation Charlie's chances don't look good and, if he suffers any more, he will have to be put down.

Reflecting on the day's events Fiona echoes sentiments expressed by fellow student Mike Sandiford when confronted with the euthanasia issue during his stint at the PDSA. 'It's particularly awkward watching a drama like this unfold. Talking to a client about putting their animal to sleep is perhaps easier if you are the vet in control. You are focused on the job. But if you're a student you're watching the client's grief, and it really gets to you.'

By the following day Charlie's condition has stabilised. The drip has solved the dehydration problem and he is a little more perky. X-rays show that the foreign body may have moved a little. But only a little, and the underlying problem remains.

Fiona, meanwhile, is having a day at the races. She has gone to nearby Uttoxeter. It is an uneventful race meeting, but it results in another kind of meeting that provides a fascinating opportunity to swap stories about the Bristol Veterinary School, past and present.

Fiona spends the day in the company of John Davis, who has been the Uttoxeter course vet for 20 years. More interestingly, from the student's point of view, it is 36 years since he qualified from Bristol. The memories are still vivid – particularly of a certain Professor of Surgery. 'I think probably the only member of staff who is still there would be Harold Pearson. I suppose it's quite remarkable there's even one left, given the fact that I was there in 1960 and you are there in 1996.'

Fiona tells John that Professor Pearson is due to retire in a few months' time but that for now he shows few signs of either slowing down or giving up. 'He does a two-hour lecture in one hour and whizzes through it. At the end of it I feel like my pen's on fire.'

'He was a lecturer in surgery when I was there, not a professor', says John Davis. 'He was a very dogmatic chap as I remember. But I think students quite like that. They like to be told "never" or "always". I suppose some students wouldn't like his approach, but I always thought it was first class.'

A knowing smile spreads across Fiona's face. It really is extraordinary that one lecturer could have such an influence on two students a generation apart. It is difficult to imagine any Bristol veterinary student forgetting Professor Pearson. 'I still remember some of his dos and don'ts', continues John. '"Never use a whelping forceps. Always examine a cow for mastitis. Always squeeze a dog's anal glands. Make sure a horse is vaccinated against tetanus." Now *that* sort of dogma students like. It certainly worked on me. I still remember it 36 years later.'

Predictably, though, Professor Harold Pearson remains perhaps the only constant in a veterinary school that has changed beyond all recognition since John Davis's time. Then there were 24 students; now there are 66. Then only one in six of them were women. Today women account for more than half of the fifth-year students.

John remembers the school as being a little isolated and rather claustrophobic – a memory which still has plenty of resonance for today's students. He is interested to know where most of the students live. On or off site? Off site, says Fiona, with male and female students often sharing houses. It was very different in his day. 'We all had to live in at Langford. And the four girls were all locked up at night in a separate wing. I don't know if it was to keep us away from them or them away from us', says John, roaring with laughter.

The next day Fiona is back in Litchfield at the Pool House Veterinary Hospital, involved in some desperate, last-minute fund-raising. Whatever Charlie the puppy has swallowed is firmly lodged. His condition is deteriorating. Surgery is now his only chance of survival, but Lisa Mason, his owner, cannot lay her hands on enough cash to finance the operation. Sometimes in cases like this the People's Dispensary for Sick Animals will pay. But not this time. To qualify for help pet owners have to be claiming benefit. Lisa earns very little, but she claims no state benefits.

Fortunately she has a resourceful and highly determined vet on her side. Dougie Fountain telephones the RSPCA with the story. Can they help? Yes, possibly, but first it will be necessary to interview Lisa to get a first-hand account of the circumstances. No time for that, says Dougie; he has to operate immediately. The RSPCA is sympathetic and agrees to make a donation. Now all Dougie and Fiona need is the go-ahead from Lisa. She gives her consent, and within an hour Charlie is in theatre.

What follows is a lengthy and complicated operation. The foreign body turns out to be a cassette tape which, though it might sound comic, is very bad news indeed. The plastic casing is nowhere to be seen – probably passed out during the puppy's motions. But the audio tape itself is still very much in evidence – tough, indigestible and unbroken. It is actually wound around Charlie's tongue but is hidden from view because over the course of a week skin has grown over it. The tape then stretches down the dog's throat and continues on through the small intestine and into the bowel.

'It's a real mess', Dougie tells Fiona. 'Charlie would have been a dead pup if he had been left another couple of days.'

'It must be a really unusual case', says Fiona.

'Well, yes and no', replies Dougie. 'I've actually had a dog swallow a cassette once before. Much more common, though, is cats swallowing needle and thread. Happens all the time when owners leave their sewing lying around, and that can be very nasty.'

Pulling and disentangling the tape from Charlie's insides is a painstaking job. Once Dougie is satisfied that they are on top of it, Fiona is dispatched to update Lisa, who is waiting anxiously outside the operating theatre.

'It's good news', she says. 'The operation is still going on, but we've identified the problem and think we can sort it out.' When Fiona mentions the cassette Lisa doesn't know whether to laugh or cry. She buries her head in her hands. 'Oh, I can't believe it. Which tape?' The disbelief is genuine, the question is a joke and the relief is twofold: 'I'm so relieved Charlie is going to be ok. But I'm also relieved that the foreign body is not a personal belonging. Before you came out I was thinking to myself, oh, *please* don't let it be a pair of my pants!'

Now both women are laughing. It emerges that the deal that's been struck with the RSPCA involves Lisa Mason paying just half of what is likely to be a £300 bill. Even that won't be so easy, but for now Lisa is simply overjoyed. 'I couldn't be happier. We're going to celebrate tonight. The money side of things will be hard, I know it will. I'll have to do lots of extra hours at work. But it's worth it because Charlie is my little boy.'

A couple of days later Charlie is much better. The drip has gone and the appetite and energy are back. When Lisa comes to collect him he leaps into her arms and plants a paw on each shoulder. Fiona has a souvenir for her – a clear plastic bag stuffed with several yards of audio tape. 'From now on I've got to move everything out of his way', says a chastened Lisa. Then, nuzzling her face against his, she affects a half-hearted attempt to scold him. 'You're a *naughty* Charlie as well as a cheeky Charlie. But I'm over the moon to be taking you home. I just didn't think it would be possible when I brought you in a couple of days ago.'

As Lisa heads for home Fiona heads away from home, down the M6 and M5 towards Bristol and then on to Langford and the veterinary school. The time for learning and revision is running out. Exams are nearly upon her. The next few weeks will determine whether she and 65 other students are good enough to make the grade. 'It's a time of real tension and seemingly endless hard work', says Fiona. 'I just want it to be all over now.'

Those sentiments are echoed by Trude Mostue, who is having a particularly stressful Easter break. For her there has been no opportunity to escape to a different environment because she has had to stay put, redoing her clerking week on small-animal practice. It is the price she must pay for failing first time round. And for Trude it is a very high price indeed. She knows that she is one of the students most likely to fail her finals. So, understandably, she would rather be spending all her time revising. But there is another reason too. Of all the students at Langford, Trude is perhaps the one who feels and worries most about the sometimes claustrophobic atmosphere. This Easter the nearest she has come to getting away from it all is her regular sessions at the gym.

Trude has never quite fitted in with what some might regard as the 'typical Langford student'. At 28 she is older than most and reluctant to embrace much of the social life on offer at the University. Her relative maturity is evident in the life she follows away from the academic round. Trude's home, for example, is not your typical chaotic student crash-pad. She lives in a neat and tidy Victorian terrace in the nearby Somerset town of Yatton.

This morning she is sipping herbal tea and trying to catch up with a bit of revision before heading off to Langford four miles down the road. 'Today's the first day of my small-animal practice week – again!' she says, directing her comments at the man reading the breakfast news on the television in the corner of the room.

Trude has spent the first fortnight of the holidays revising but is worried about how much she is actually taking in. There isn't enough time. Where do the days go, she wonders. 'I feel like I'm doing a hundred things at once. Being stressed, trying to relax, revising for my finals, thinking about animal practice … ' Her voice trails off. She's trying to work out how much time she has left. It is six weeks before her first exam and Trude begins some basic multiplication out loud. 'Six weeks. That's six times seven, which equals 42 days. It's just too little time left. I'm panicking, really panicking. I was panicking last night. I couldn't sleep.'

'Panic' and 'stress' are becoming familiar words in Trude's vocabulary, the result of the many mounting pressures. But there was a particular reason she couldn't sleep last night – her parents. They had called her from Norway. 'Every time I speak to my parents they ask me how it's going. And yesterday they asked me, "Are we going to buy tickets for the tenth of July?", which is graduation day. I just said I didn't know.'

For Trude Mostue this is a time of real tension and doubt. She talks frequently about the possibility of failing her finals but remains determined to qualify as a vet. If she fails in July, she reasons, she can always resit in September. Somehow, some way and sooner or later she will realise her ambition. There are no doubts about *that* in her mind.

Driving to the veterinary school in her old, battered and temperamental Nissan, Trude makes it clear that she is keen to escape from the collegiate atmosphere and start paid employment in the 'real' world. 'I'm fed up with the vet school. Even when I'm away from it, driving round the area, I feel sick every time I see a signpost to Langford. It's a very small place and you just really need some space.'

By nature Trude is gregarious and fun-loving. She is certainly no loner, but at Langford the Norwegian student has become something of an outsider. It could be her age or her nationality – perhaps a combination of both factors. At the moment she does not feel comfortable in the university environment. 'I get really concerned about being

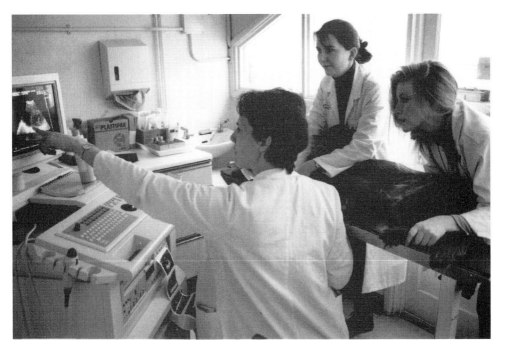

Keeping a cool head despite the mounting pressures. Trude reads an ultrasound.

a foreigner. Sometimes it would be nice to be like everyone else. English!'

Someone she does feel comfortable with is Alison Blaxter, Head of the Small Animal Practice and her personal tutor. The circumstances in which they meet this morning are less than ideal – it was Alison's decision to make Trude redo her week of small-animal practice. However, whatever her reservations about some of the other teachers, Trude is a big fan of Alison's. 'She has always been very fair, helpful and supportive with me. And though I'd rather not be here this week, she was right to make me come back and do this again.'

Trude goes into the waiting room to collect the first patient of the day. In fact there are two, both belonging to the same owner but sitting – restrained – on opposite sides of the room. Paddy is an eleven-month-old cocker spaniel and Pippa is a six-year-old collie.

The dogs share the same house, but that is about all they have in common. They are involved in a constant struggle for dominance and consequently they frequently fight. They've been at it again today

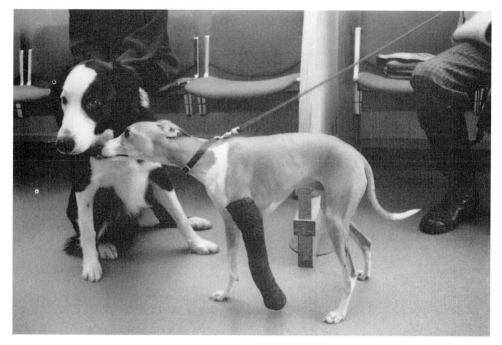

Unlike Pippa and Paddy, these two see eye to eye.

– the second time this week. Their owner wants their wounds healed and their behaviour improved.

Trude takes the young cocker spaniel into the consulting room first. Paddy turns out to be a rather excitable young bitch who is difficult to control during the examination. While Alison Blaxter looks on through the 'spy' window from an adjoining room, the student struggles to keep her patient's head still long enough to examine an eye wound sustained during the fight. Despite the traces of blood, it isn't too serious and, although there are also some punctures inside her ears, it seems that Paddy has escaped lightly.

Her opponent hasn't been quite as lucky and is suffering rather more – with a bruised neck and a swollen and punctured leg. As the older of the two animals, it is Pippa who should be top dog. Things have become nasty because Paddy has chosen to challenge the normal hierarchy. For the physical wounds Trude prescribes antibiotics, after first checking her diagnosis with Alison. But the psychological scars and grievances both animals are now nursing won't heal so easily.

The owner explains that Paddy and Pippa have never cared too much for each other and in the last few months open warfare appears to have broken out. The fights they are having are both vicious and regular. Neither dog has shown any aggression towards the owner and her family. 'They love us – they just hate each other.'

Alison explains what she calls 'the principles of managing aggression within a household'. 'It's all to do with pack management', she says. 'Dogs are pack animals and the reason they squabble within their family – whether it's biting people or biting each other – is to do with disputes in the hierarchy. Who's the top dog?'

'I think the younger dog, Paddy, is becoming top dog', says the owner.

Alison is concerned. 'Usually it's the oldest dog if they're of equal weight and size, which these two are. It should be Pippa, and we need to find a way of helping her to reassert her authority as top dog.'

The suggested solution is going to be a rude shock for Paddy. 'You must do everything with and for Pippa first. *She* goes through the door first, she gets attention first, she gets fed first. The golden rule is that they never take turns. Pippa must always be top dog.'

For Trude, who has been listening intently throughout the conversation, this has been an interesting lesson. 'It's fascinating to see a behavioural problem. It reminds you the small-animal practice isn't just surgery and medicine.'

Much of it, though, is routine. And it is to practise and master some of the routine work that Trude has returned on this clerking week. In particular, her problems with injections are fresh in the memory and still capable of prompting embarrassment. But not for long. Ben, a strikingly hairy crossbred dog that has recently been acquired by its owner from an animal rescue home, provides an early opportunity to banish the spectre of a mis-targeted needle. The dog needs a checkup and a booster vaccination. No problem. This time there is no injecting through the scruff of the neck. Trude goes about her work with confidence and efficiency. It is to be the pattern for the rest of her time on the small-animal practice clerking rotation.

At the end of the week Trude sits in Alison Blaxter's office waiting for the tutor to arrive. She doesn't know yet whether she has done enough to pass. 'I'm quite happy about the week, though I can think of some points I might be criticised for. But that's fair enough. In general, though, I think it was better than last time. But you never know.'

At this point Alison breezes into the office, smiling and apologising for being late. There is a slight feeling of *déjà vu* as she goes through the preamble that must accompany all assessments – everything is negotiable, let me know if you feel you have been misjudged, any criticisms I may make are supposed to be helpful.

As it turns out, there isn't a great deal of criticism this time. 'Overall, I've been very pleased with what you've done this week. It was a lot better than the previous one.' Alison praises Trude for being well prepared, helpful, enthusiastic and conscientious. She is also impressed with her consultation technique and is satisfied that Trude's practical skills are improving too. 'We've seen you give a lot of injections. You're competent now. Only two things now mar your performance. You still lack a little confidence about your competence, and the second thing is that you need a little more practice.'

One of the most noticeable areas of improvement is in what Alison calls Trude's 'verbal communication'. Her language skills have consistently been identified as a problem, and the student herself has frequently acknowledged that she struggles with her English when she is under pressure. Not much cause for concern about that this time, according to Alison. 'You were very relaxed with clients and relayed information to them concisely. Much better than last time. Very impressive.'

After this, the conclusion to the assessment is no surprise. Trude Mostue has passed her small-animal practice clerking rotation at the second attempt. It will be this success rather than the last failure which will be included in her personal file. She is delighted. 'I'm very pleased with that. If you've prepared for something and you've worked hard and you see some good results, it is very satisfying. At the moment I really need that kind of encouragement in general. It gives me confidence to face what lies ahead. Maybe I'm going to be a vet after all.'

Job hunting

THE VET'S TRADE MAGAZINE, *The Veterinary Record*, is not designed to entice. It is an appropriately sober and serious scientific journal with headlines like CONTROL OF BOVINE TOXOPLASMOSIS and MALIGNANT HISTIOCYTOSIS IN BERNESE MOUNTAIN DOGS. Those who part with £2.75 for their copy are not expecting a racy read.

However, towards the back of the magazine there is a dramatic change in style. The prose is suddenly and somewhat bizarrely transformed from the prosaic to the purple. Out go sentences that alert readers to 'Antigenic types of canine parvoviruses prevailing in Taiwan', to be replaced by enticements such as 'The Lake District, a vast playground on your doorstep'. No, this isn't the travel section. It's the job adverts.

The shortage of qualified vets in Britain has prompted private practices to try their hand at copywriting advertisements. The results, to put it diplomatically, are uneven. With an enthusiasm that can appear to border on the desperate, the technique frequently involves selling the area as hard as the practice: 'The Yorkshire experience. Between city lights and Peak District hills we have a super mixed practice', or 'Durham Cathedral City. Beautiful countryside at hand. Excellent state and private schools.'

The adverts are peppered with lots of other enticements too. 'Friendly competent nurses, lots of toys and pleasant clients.' (These 'toys', of course, wouldn't be found in your average *crèche* – they are the kind trained, grown-up vets play with.) 'Two recent graduates and lots of lovely nurses to provide a caring service for our patients.' 'We want our staff to enjoy their work; hence newly built, comfortable air-conditioned premises; fully furnished house away from surgery;

mobile phone to allow life to continue while on call; car allowance.'

All this amounts to pretty clear evidence that the most intense competition for jobs is not between prospective employees but among the employers. It puts students in a strong position – with the very brightest, like Alison Lee, apparently able to pick and choose. Well, not quite. Alison may be one of the high-flyers at Langford this year, but her choices are rather more restricted than one might have imagined.

Alison has begun her job hunting early because she is determined to find employment close to the veterinary school. Her fiancé, Craig Beck, who graduated from Langford last year, has chosen to work at a practice nearby – a decision prompted in large measure by a desire to be close to the school during Alison's last year. Now she must reciprocate by finding a job in the area. The two of them have decided to begin married life and their veterinary careers in the West Country.

This reduces Alison's options considerably. However, she might be in luck as a local practice is looking for an assistant. It could be just what she is looking for, only a short distance from the house she will share with Craig in Yatton.

On the morning of her interview Alison takes a rare break from revision and relaxes at home with Craig. The two of them met on her second day at the University and they have been together ever since – nearly five years now. They plan to marry soon after Alison graduates and, not surprisingly, they have many shared personal and professional ambitions.

However, there are significant differences in their approach to their chosen career. Alison says she has wanted to be a vet since the age of seven. 'It's a real vocation,' she enthuses, 'I can't ever remember wanting to be anything else.' Craig can. He thought about all sorts of things until, one day, a teacher told him he was probably clever enough to be a vet, so he thought he would have a go. By then he was 16 and about to sit his GCSEs. 'I didn't really have a vocational calling from a young age', Craig remembers. 'However, once I made up my mind to do it I became very committed very quickly and I really like the job now.'

However, Craig remains the more laid-back character when it comes to his career. He certainly isn't as ambitious as his future wife. 'I'm not a career vet – I don't feel I have to have my own practice by the age of 28 …. For me it's more a way of life than a career.'

By contrast, Alison is determined to 'get on'. She wants to study for further veterinary qualifications and, typically, has set herself a number of personal and professional goals. 'I'm very career-minded, but at the same time I don't want to miss out on the other things in life. I want a family as well – and not a family who don't know me because I spend all my time at work. I couldn't be happy with just my career and I couldn't be happy with just my family. I believe if I work hard enough I can have both.'

If effort alone can guarantee personal and professional happiness, Alison Lee's cup should overflow. Her capacity for hard work is almost legendary at the vet school. In the run-up to her finals she thinks nothing of revising for up to 14 hours a day. It is a pattern that has been maintained throughout her five years on the course. 'I wouldn't say I was the best student,' says Alison, 'but I do work very hard and always set myself challenges – personal goals. I know some people find this difficult to believe, but I actually enjoy the studying'. The only problem she has is knowing when to call a halt. 'I find it hard to stop myself working too much. If I don't make a conscious effort to stop I would just be working all the time. So I have to make myself go out sometimes.'

Alison wants some interview tips from Craig. He doesn't claim a great deal of expertise, having got the first job he applied for. However, he reminds her that she should be asking as many questions as she is asked and also urges her to find out in detail about salary and perks. 'Don't forget to ask about the car they're offering and whether there's petrol for private use as well. The job is important, but so is the financial package.'

Five years of further education have left most of the students with a legacy of debt and now, understandably, they are anxious to begin the process of making themselves financially solvent as soon as possible. The government does make a contribution towards the cost of their education, but it is very much just that – a contribution. As any student or parent will tell you, it is nowhere near enough to cover the entire cost. Indeed, at about £1800 a year it doesn't even pay the rent. So the rest has to be made up from parents' pockets and student loans.

'My parents have given me enough so I can live a comfortable life,' says Alison, 'but I can't afford to live an extravagant life because I know

I am spending their money.' Alison's annual rent is £2000, and she reckons that even living frugally she needs £4000 a year in all. 'I've budgeted fairly well and I haven't come out with my debts too horrendous, although they're still fairly bad – I owe about £8000. But as you get towards the end of the course you don't feel so bad about being in debt because you know you'll soon be able to start paying it off.'

Craig is already beginning to feel 'more comfortably off'. A year into his first job he has a 'decent' salary, a company car and a rent-free three-bedroomed house, which he and Alison will share. But during the first year he finds he has also been on a steep learning curve. 'The University gives you some information which is often useful – but not always.' 'What's the main difference?' asks Alison. 'The clients', he replies without hesitation.

The Bristol Veterinary School has always recognised that this is likely to be the case. Clerking and foster practice are designed to give students a taste of dealing with the public, but there is no substitute for experience. And the only real experience begins the first time a young vet finds himself or herself alone and totally responsible for a client.

Predictably, Craig has found it difficult on occasions to speak the owner's 'language'. Translating veterinary science into everyday English can present real difficulties, particularly for a student straight out of the academic atmosphere of Langford. There have been some surprises too. 'I actually found it quite difficult to get used to charging clients at first', says Craig. 'It seemed quite expensive. But then you realise it is a business and that there are lots of costs to be covered.'

Before leaving for her interview, Alison pays particular attention to what she will wear. One earring in each ear instead of the usual two and a plain white blouse and dark trousers rather than the familiar jeans and T-shirt. 'Going for jobs like this, you want to come across as the sort of person you'll be in practice. Your clothes have to be both smart and practical – which rules out jeans and skirts.'

Alison readily admits that she is nervous. It is her first interview for five years, the last being when she applied for a place at the veterinary school. She assumes that today's interview will be more about her personality than her knowledge. 'They won't be able to tell what I'm like

Thinking things through. Alison Lee deals with an ear problem.

at surgery or consultation from just one meeting. I suppose I'm worried that they may not like me. But then it's also important that I like them. It's a two-way thing.'

Before she leaves the house Alison carefully folds up a neatly written note reminding her of the questions she wants answered at the interview: salary, car, house, rota, surgery times, holidays.

The practice is just a few minutes' drive from Craig's house. It is run by Liz Watkins, who greets Alison at reception before taking her on a guided tour of the surgery. It is well equipped, modern and expanding. The interview itself is conducted in private, but before the two of them disappear behind closed doors it is clear that both women are anxious to make this work. The location and the facilities suit Alison, and Liz could be on the point of attracting an honours graduate from Langford.

Afterwards Alison is clearly enthusiastic. 'I really liked it. Liz Watkins was really friendly and keen to make a good impression. She seemed happy to allow the assistant to be on the same level as her – I wouldn't have to do all the antisocial shifts.'

The salary Liz is offering is £16,000 a year, which includes the housing allowance. Alison doesn't need a house because she will be living in the one provided free by Craig's practice. The car she would be offered is an E-registration Ford Escort, with petrol for business and private local use paid for. 'The salary and the car are ok', says Alison, '... not as good as some jobs, but I'd rather take a lower salary and feel I was happy in my job. The most important thing for me at the moment is to see some progression in my career. I want the opportunity to learn new surgical techniques and to assist in more difficult operations.'

Liz Watkins has interviewed four other candidates and has promised to let Alison know the outcome in the next few days – an interval that Alison, too, will be using to make up her mind. She is interested, but at this stage will go only as far as saying that were she offered the job there is a 'strong possibility' she would accept. First, though, she wants to sleep on it and talk to Craig.

He rings her soon after she gets home. The conversation is brief because he is having a busy day at work.

'What was it like?' he asks.

'It was fine.'

'What about the money?'

'Sixteen.'

'And the car?'

'An E-reg Escort. She says it's fairly reliable.'

'Does she sound interested?'

'I think so, but it's hard to tell. Who knows?'

The following day Alison does know. Liz Watkins rings her.

'We'd very much like you to join us here. I don't know if you've had time to think about it?'

'Yes, I've been thinking long and hard', Alison replies. 'I didn't want to rush into it, I wanted to be sure. I was a bit worried about coming in as a new graduate. But I'm sure you'll all make me very welcome and you're obviously a very happy team.'

'Yes, we'll try and help you and offer as much support as possible.'

'We'll, I'd like to accept your offer then please.'

'That's great! I'm really pleased.'

And so is Alison. It is a big weight off her mind knowing she has secured a job close to her fiancé's practice. But she is also well aware that her decision has taken a lot of pressure off her future employer. 'She was really relieved because she obviously wanted me to take the job.'

Alison is keen to begin work as soon as possible. So she has agreed to start at the beginning of August, barely a month after she gets the results of her finals. 'I'm just going to plunge in at the deep end and see how it goes. I'm looking forward to it. First, though, I have to get my degree.'

Passing her finals is likely to be something of a formality. But for Alison Lee simply passing isn't enough. The challenge she has set herself is to pass with honours. At the moment she is revising in two places, dividing her time between the flat she shares with Fiona Green in Wrington and the house she will share with Craig in Yatton.

Alison's approach to revision is very methodical. She converts textbook information into her own notes and then reads and re-reads them. She reckons it takes between 20 and 30 minutes to learn a page once she has 'converted' it. For her exams last year she had 140 pages to revise. This year the task is much more daunting – even for the workaholic she admits to being. She estimates that there are 600 pages which must be learnt for her finals.

Like all the students at Langford she is feeling the pressure and admits to bouts of 'irrational behaviour and tetchiness' with even her closest friends, Craig included. However, she also knows that it is her student friends who she will miss most when she finally leaves the veterinary school to begin her new job. 'The difficult thing now is that we've only got about a month left and it would be really nice to socialise with other people on the course who you've become really friendly with. Unfortunately, all we've got time to do right now is revise. That's quite sad.'

Craig agrees. Students completing their degree course at Langford develop a strong sense of camaraderie, and it is one of the things he misses most about professional life away from the school. 'The saddest part about qualifying is that all your friends are scattered around the country. You stay in touch of course, but you really miss that regular daily contact.'

Alison knows she will miss the teachers as well. She is well aware that some students in her year have not always been complimentary about certain members of staff. However, while she concedes that the current crop of fifth-years has been particularly outspoken in some of its criticism, Alison and most of her colleagues have come to appreciate the expertise and help provided by the specialist teaching staff. 'I would certainly like to think that in 20 years' time I might be as good as some of the surgeons at Langford. I think your respect for them grows throughout the course.'

The next few months in Alison's life will be momentous ones. Finals, her first job and marriage. When she and Craig walk down the aisle they will be following a well-trodden veterinary path. Statistics indicate than one in four vets will marry another vet. 'Hardly surprising given the incestuous atmosphere at Langford', observes Craig.

Joint incomes and shared interests offer the prospect of a comfortable and mutually supportive relationship. They won't be short of money and should have an intimate understanding of the pressures of each other's work. However, neither Craig nor Alison is viewing the future through rose-tinted spectacles. They have a realistic sense of the difficulties ahead too. Both of them know they will be working in a profession that will make enormous demands on their time. So how will they cope? Characteristically, Alison believes that the key to success and future happiness is organisation and hard work. 'We'll have to work at it of course. Hopefully we'll be able to sort out our rotas so we're both off together. I think as long as we plan ahead and make the most of our time off, then we should be happy.'

The pursuit of happiness is an ambition which Alison Lee has never lost sight of. Clever, highly motivated and hard-working she may be, but what she is not is a dull school swot. Alison is a woman who attracts admiration and affection from peers and teachers alike because she has an appetite for a challenge and a real capacity for enjoying herself. As she nears the end of her time at the Bristol Veterinary School, the memories are of five great years. 'They've been the best days of my life so far. I'm hoping in the future that I'll be as happy as I am now.'

Finals

FIVE AND A HALF WEEKS after the fifth-year students return from their Easter holidays finals are upon them. The tension can be unbearable. A few years ago one student actually fled from an exam. Fortunately she was pursued out of the building by Professor Harold Pearson, who is not always the intimidating figure that some of the students imagine him to be. Indeed, he managed to coax her back by offering to let her sit the paper in his office. 'She passed quite easily and is now a very good vet. But it does illustrate what a stressful time it is for many of the students.'

Professor Pearson is responsible for compiling the exam paper on surgery. Finals, he says, have become much more difficult in the last five years. There has been a deliberate attempt to make them more demanding after it was felt that the honours degree was becoming devalued because 'too many' students were achieving the necessary standard.

The Bristol Veterinary School fervently hopes that none of its students will fail. However, experience suggests there are likely to be some disappointed candidates. After five years it can be a crushing blow to fall at the last hurdle. So why do students fail? 'Well, sometimes they just don't do the work', says Dr Kieran O'Brien. 'They have to carry quite a large amount of factual information for their finals. It's a bit of a slog. And sometimes people just don't want to do that. That's the main reason students fail.'

To the relief of all the students the clerking rotations are coming to an end. With these out of the way, they can concentrate full time on revision for their degree exams. By now the 40 women and 26 men who make up the final year have demonstrated some aptitude for the practical nature of the job that lies ahead. They have been formally assessed and graded. All of them have passed all their clerking weeks.

Now they can prepare for their finals without further distractions. It may be a relief to be freed from the responsibilities of clerking, but their re-entry into full-time academic study is the most nerve-racking time of their entire five years at the vet school.

Can anything be done to relieve the tension? Probably not, according to PDSA vet Eamon Draper, who is bidding a final farewell to some of his Langford students. He remembers his finals all too well and reckons it is an experience that the fifth-years simply have to face and live through. The stress, the worry and the sleepless nights are an integral and unavoidable part of the experience. So how did he get through it, the students ask. 'I don't really know', says Eamon. 'But I certainly remember the main topic of conversation was how much money you would be prepared to pay to bypass your finals. At the stage you lot are at now, it was around £5000. But of course that's several weeks before the exam. Two days before our finals £5000 had risen to £20,000, and on the actual day of the first exam several of us had decided that it was worth abandoning a career as a vet rather than sit the dreaded exams!'

The moral of Eamon's story is not 'jack it all in now – you're doomed' but rather 'it may look bleak, but hang on in there and you'll be all right'. It is not a distant memory for him, and because he is young enough to remember clearly and share their feelings, Langford's anxious fifth-year students seem to draw some comfort from what he has to say.

Ultimately, though, sympathy, empathy and support – however welcome – are not going to be enough to propel the young veterinary colts and mares down the final furlong of what has been a very long academic race. This is the bit that they must do on their own. Trude Mostue, for one, doesn't mind. 'Now I can shut myself away and not talk to anyone else. I don't have to think about anything except revision, and for me that's good.'

In these last few weeks Trude has become a creature of the night. In the early evening she might call in for a quick session at the gym. But then it is back to her house in Yatton and a night of revision and herbal tea. Usually during these concentrated periods of studying, night gives way to day. Trude rarely goes to bed before 5 a.m. 'I think it's a really good time to learn things. It's much easier to concentrate when it's dark and there's not much happening. I admit it's a bit dodgy, though, when I have to do something during the daytime now because I don't really function.'

Mike Sandiford's routine is less nocturnal, but he too has completely immersed himself in revision. His approach is novel, consisting of sitting cross-legged on the floor with papers covering almost every inch of the carpet. 'I suppose you couldn't really call it a technique,' he laughs, 'and it takes ages to sort everything out when I want to gather up the papers.' Mike, though, isn't a great believer in techniques or systems for swotting. 'It's basically down to hard work. That's the only secret to success in exams that I know.'

The atmosphere around the vet school, he says, is more one of nervous anticipation than blind panic, although the state of mind varies from one student to another. 'Some people are as cool as a cucumber and some are really stressed, which can be really counterproductive. I reckon I'm somewhere in the middle.'

He is also particularly excited this morning because he may be on the verge of clinching a rather exotic job. For the first three years he was at university Mike shared a house with a veterinary student who had begun the course a couple of years ahead of him. When she qualified she flew off to Botswana to work on a game reserve. A fortnight ago she wrote to Mike saying her employers were looking for another newly qualified vet. Was he interested? Of course he is interested. And today, after an exchange of faxes, the people who run the game reserve have confirmed that the interest is mutual. In two months' time Mike may be out of Langford and off to Africa.

On the reserve his main job would be to look after orphaned wild animals and be the veterinary assistant on an ostrich farm. 'Yes, an ostrich farm! I can't quite believe it. I think I probably didn't pay too much attention during the 15 minutes of one lecture which referred to ostriches. I wasn't expecting it to be very useful.' Now, not only could it be very useful, it could be absolutely vital. If Mike is offered the job he is certainly going to have to become better acquainted with the veterinary challenges posed by ostriches.

Botswana sounds like a real adventure and Mike would jump on a plane at the first opportunity. 'I'm really very excited about the possibility of going, though I'm not sure what they expect really. I mean, I don't have five or ten years' experience ... I'm pretty green. The thought of going out there by myself and basically being the vet is a bit nerve-racking.'

First, though, there is the more immediate challenge of qualifying. The constant working is a routine he has grown used to during the fifth year. 'There's precious little spare time throughout the final year. Normally I'm a pretty sociable person, but this is the first year when I haven't put my friends first.'

Mike has made a calculation that only by forgoing regular social pleasures like trips to the pub will he find enough time to complete the long slog – which really started seven years ago when he began studying for his A levels at 16. Now, at 23, he is not about to fall at the final hurdle. 'Like everyone else here, there was a period of adjustment when I arrived. Suddenly, from being the best student at school I was in the bottom half at university. That said, though, I haven't failed an exam yet and I should pass.'

What Trude Mostue would do for Mike Sandiford's quiet confidence! Ever since they shared a week on large-animal practice the differences between them have been obvious. It is since that time that Kieran O'Brien has suspected that Mike will pass with ease and that Trude will probably fail. Hardly surprising, then, that she is fretting about her finals and trying to convince herself that failure is only a temporary thing. 'It's not the end of the world if I don't pass. I can always resit in the autumn. But then again, my whole family are coming over from Norway for graduation in the summer – including now my two sisters.'

Perhaps Trude's biggest problem is nerves. And, when she's nervous, her normally impressive grasp of the English language seems to slip away. To try to prepare herself for what lies ahead Trude will be sitting a mock exam. Finals are a mixture of written papers, practical work and oral examinations. It is this last ordeal that Trude fears most, so teacher and examiner Sue Shaw has prepared a mock viva for her this morning.

Trude is taking it seriously. She is smartly dressed and concentrating hard. If it is to be useful, she has to behave as if to all intents and purposes it is real. However, before the test begins Sue offers a few tips on what to do when it is really real. 'Try to relax. When you first arrive in this room be prepared for some small talk. There'll be two examiners. You'll know one of them and the other will be an external person. They'll probably start by asking you what you're planning to do in your holidays, that sort of thing. Use that time to settle in.'

Sue also explains that the viva is an opportunity to correct any disasters that may have occurred during the written exam. If a student has answered a question incorrectly on paper he or she may well be invited to attempt a correct answer during the interview.

Trude seems reassured and so Sue Shaw begins the mock viva. The student is presented with a number of case histories and is expected to deliver a diagnosis, course of treatment and prognosis. A picture of a cocker spaniel puppy is illuminated on an overhead projector.

'He's ten weeks old', says Sue. 'The owners got him from a reputable breeder. At first he was fine but then he went off his food and 24 hours later began vomiting. What kind of condition is he in now?'

'Dehydrated', says Trude.

'What kind of fluids would he need?'

'Electrolytes.'

'Any particular electrolytes?'

'Potassium, sodium.'

'He's very young, so should you be doing anything else as well?'

Trude is momentarily stumped. The quick-fire exchange has ground to a standstill and is replaced by silence – the kind of silence that any student in a viva dreads. But Trude remains composed, and then suddenly she remembers. 'What about nutrients?'

'Yes, but what kind of nutrients?'

'Glucose.'

Sue keeps the questions coming and feeds new information into the case history, continually probing the student's depth of knowledge. But her approach is neither confrontational nor adversarial, and even when Trude cannot answer a question she continues gently to prompt and encourage.

When it is finished the examiner is keen to know the student's thoughts. Not this time her thoughts about veterinary science, but rather about the experience of the viva. 'Because this is only a practice viva I have to ask you whether you have any particular worries about the procedure.'

'I've been really worried about not finding the right words, losing my way', replies Trude. 'My big fear is that my mind will simply go blank. But I feel ok about that now.'

'There will always be a way to get round those blackouts', says Sue reassuringly. 'You're not alone in suffering from this problem. You actually made it very obvious when you didn't know something and that gave me an opportunity to ask you another question which you could answer.'

'Is that a good thing to do then?' asks Trude.

'Yes,' says Sue, before adding the very important rider, '… as long as you don't do it too often!' The two women both laugh. 'If you're as relaxed during the exam as you have been in the mock you won't have a problem.' Trude is grateful for the practice and the reassurance, although she's acutely aware that there is no substitute for the real thing. 'Thanks for all your help. It's been really good. But I know next time we meet like this it's going to be much more tense.'

Tension now pervades the whole Langford site. It is just a few days away from the first exam, a rectal viva in which students will be expected to perform an internal examination on a cow and judge whether it is pregnant.

Meanwhile, Professor Harold Pearson is putting the finishing touches to his preparations for the last surgery exams he will supervise before retirement. He knows the students are anxious and is sympathetic, but only up to a point. It is his view that many of them over-react. Nearly 50 years ago, when the Professor sat his own finals, he remembers the atmosphere as being very different. 'I was quite confident actually. I wasn't in the least bit nervous about exams. Students these days are abnormally nervous about their finals. They have medical treatment for depression, some of them. I don't think there's any need for it.'

It may not be a necessity, but it is a fact of student life at the Bristol Veterinary School. Student advisor Julia Trevett knows all about it. It is her job to listen and counsel students about any problems they may be facing. She has become a sort of unofficial agony aunt, and the students love her for it. This morning Fiona Green has gone to see her to discuss hiring a gown for her graduation.

'How's it going at the moment?' Julia asks Fiona as the student paces around her office. 'Sit down for a minute. Are you ok?'

'I'm ok, but the atmosphere is pretty tense at the moment.'

'The students all seem to be reasonably calm', says Julia. 'I don't detect any real panic.'

On this occasion Fiona is reluctant to agree with the observations of the student advisor. 'I don't know about things being reasonably calm. I think they're all quietly not calm. The thing is I think that everybody goes through a phase of being ok and then suddenly it hits them. I woke up this morning and thought, oh God!'

Julia Trevett offers what reassurance she can and then encourages Fiona to try on her gown. Fiona seems unsure. 'Shall I? All right then.' 'It fits,' says Julia, 'looks fine.' Fiona is now standing rather self-consciously in the middle of the office clothed in the gown that she hopes to be wearing come graduation day. And the incongruity of it suddenly hits her. 'Oh God, what does it look like? This really is tempting fate.'

Steve Leonard might be tempting fate too. In the house he shares with five other students, including Julie Richards, he exudes confidence.

'These exams are going to be some of the easiest we've done – all the teachers say so', he says.

Julie laughs, unconvinced by Steve's confidence.

'No, really they are', he insists. 'I haven't heard any bad stories about people sitting their finals.'

'How about the four people who failed last year?' asks Julie.

'Well there is that I suppose', concedes Steve.

However, he is not to be deflected from his theme. In a student house where collective tension could prove overwhelming, Steve Leonard seems to have appointed himself as a one-man confidence booster. 'The kind of questions I've heard we'll be asked go something like this. "This horse has got tetanus; do you know what's wrong with it?" "Yes," you reply, "it's got tetanus." Then they say, "Well done". Honestly, there's nothing to worry about!'

An odd orderliness has settled on a normally chaotic house during the last days before exams. The students are almost apologetic about its uncharacteristic tidiness. But there is an explanation. Apparently their new-found enthusiasm for household chores is based on the theory that they need an excuse to stop revising. Cleaning up is considered an 'acceptable' excuse.

The concentrated periods of study are clearly taking their toll. It isn't easy even for students as highly motivated as these. They all have different methods. Some revise at the school, Julie Richards locks herself in her room all day, while Steve Leonard swots in the garden.

The methods may be different, but they are all agreed on the need to begin revising much earlier than for previous exams. And not just because this time they are preparing for their finals. Steve explains that the students are now contemplating life beyond university. 'The difference between these exams and ones we've done in the past is that we used to revise just to pass exams, whereas this time we're revising to pass our exams *and* to learn the stuff we'll need to know when we're out in practice.'

That could be only a couple of months away. But first they must qualify. The finals begin with a practical test – the rectal viva, or 'hands-up cows' backsides' as Kieran O'Brien describes it. The main purpose of the examination is to establish whether a cow is pregnant. Routine stuff – unless, of course, a successful outcome to five years of hard study depends on getting it right.

Trude Mostue, who has had more than her fair share of getting it wrong, is one of the first to disappear into the sheds to begin her exams. One by one all the students follow suit, emerging a quarter of an hour later to deliver their own verdict on their performance. Trude literally skips out, beaming with relief. She is uncharacteristically confident, talking quickly and breathless with excitement. 'Piece of cake. It was really easy. Well I hope it was. I only had one cow. I think I would have been given more cows if I hadn't been saying the right thing.

Maybe all the extra practice I've done during the Easter holidays has paid off.'

Now the other students are emerging too. Jon Coupe, relaxing with a cigarette, is a little more downbeat but seems to have coped with the first big test. 'It was ok. I had to do two and neither was particularly straightforward. They were very tight and I was losing the blood supply to my hand. But I think I got it right.'

So does Mike Sandiford. 'I thought I passed – but not spectacularly.' That view seems to be the common consensus among most of the students. It has been a relatively easy start to three weeks of exams. It will certainly get harder, but at least now the nervous anticipation is over. Finals are upon them.

But along with the relief and concentration on the site there is already the beginning of a sense of regret. The very word 'finals' provokes that sense, particularly for a close-knit group of students who have been together for five years. They are going to miss the collegiate atmosphere which is so much a part of life at Langford. They also know that most of them have probably asked for advice from a teacher for the last time.

Surrounded by his revision notes as he prepares for his next exam, it is Mike Sandiford who perhaps best sums up the mixed emotions. 'I've loved student life. We've all had a great time, and after five years at vet school I'm really going to miss it. We all know there's a real change of lifestyle approaching fast now. The first six months in practice is going to be very tough indeed. You've left all your friends behind and suddenly you're out there on your own and the responsibility is enormous. Every single day we're going to have to make decisions that we've never made before. It's scary, but I'm really looking forward to it. We're ready.'

All the students featured in this book, with the exception of Trude Mostue, passed their finals and are now qualified vets. Trude was one of only two students on the course to fail her exams and must re-sit them in September. Alison Lee was one of five students to pass with honours.

Facing page (clockwise from left):
Pat Ridge, now working in Penzance; Alison
Lee, working in a practice split between Nail
Sea and Yatton; Steve Leonard, still looking
for a post at the time of going to press; Fiona
Green, working in Ivybridge.

This page: (clockwise from left):
Mike Sandiford, hoping for a job in
Botswana; Trude Mostue, awaiting results at
the time of going to press; Jon Coupe, working
in a foster practice in Nottingham.

189

Index

Page numbers in italics refer to illustrations

academic excellence, emphasis on 15, 17, 127
animal behavioural problems 169
animal management, production and husbandry 132

Barr, Alistair *43*
Beck, Craig 172, 173, 174, 176, 177, 178
Benton, Steve *28*
birds, holding for examination 145
Blaxter, Dr Alison 48, 50, 51, 52, 53-4, 71-5, 167, 169, 170
Brislington 106
budgies 144-5

Caney, Sarah 55, 58-60, 61, 62, 66-8, 69-71
cardiograms *64, 131*
cats 46-54, 65-71, 144
    diabetes in cats 66-71
cattle
    calving 39-40
    feet, trimming 27, 29, 33-4
    fertility examinations 29-32, 37, 186-7
clerking rotations 23-5
    charity practice 106-28
    equine practice 76-87
    large-animal practice 23-44
    small-animal practice 45-75
    surgery 88-97
cockatoos 146
Comerford, Eithne 72, 73, *131*
communication and social skills 108, 110, 149
compassion, and economic realities 103

continuous assessment 25, 30, 133
    see also clerking rotations
counselling skills 116, 118
Coupe, Jon *14*, 15, 22, *53*, 101, 102-3, *103*, 104, *113*, 152, *158, 189*
    on compassion 103
    degree entry system, criticises 15-16
    finals, revision and 152, 187
    on Harold Pearson 102
    on Kieran O'Brien 17, 101
    PDSA clerking 106, 108-10, 118
Craig, Jane 77, 78
curriculum
    changes 130
    directed self-education (DSE) 132
    examinations 132, 133, 142, 179-87
    foster practice 137, 144-8, 149, 150, 155-65
    paraclinical subjects 132
    preclinical study 126, 130, 132
    teaching methods 132
    see also clerking rotations

Davis, John 162, 163
Davison, John 152
de Boyne Pollard, Hannah *28*
degree courses 7
    competition for places 14
    costs 130, 173
    entrance system, criticisms of 15-16
    entry qualifications 7, 130
    see also curriculum

Department of Clinical Veterinary Science 130
Dickin, Maria 119
directed self-education (DSE) 132
dogs 54-63, 146, 147, 156-62, 163-5, 167-9
    breeding age 148
    caesarean operations 58, 61, 62, 148
    dominance and 136
    nesting behaviour 55
    pack management 169
    whelping 61
Draper, Eamon 108, 109-10, 111, 112, 114, 115, 116, 117, 118, 180
Duffus, Professor Philip 8, *8*, 11, 19, 20, 99, 130, 133, 142
    career 12
    on the clerking system 24, 132-3
    on final examinations 142
    on foster-practice placements 137-8
    on practical experience 9, 17, 25, 120-1
    on students' commitment 20-1
    on students' social life 99, 104, 105
    on vets' public image 65

Easter vacation 137-70
Elliot, Sue 55, 58, 60, 61, 62, 63
employment prospects *see* jobs market
equine clerking rotation 76-87
equine diagnostic centre 23, 76, *85*, 135

euthanasia 114, 115, 116, 162

Everett, Julia 108, 109, 110

examinations
continuous assessment 25, 30, 133
exam nerves 142, 180, 184
failure, reasons for 179
finals 133, 142, 179-87
oral examinations 182-4
practical clinical assessment 133
resits 97
revision techniques 100-1, 155, 177, 181
written tests 133

'exotic' pets 106, 108, 118, 121, 145, 146

farm animals 23-44

Feline Advisory Bureau 46

feline clinical centre 46

finals 133, 142, 179-87

Fletcher, Frank and Pam 65-71

foster practice 137, 144-8, 149, 150, 155-65

Fountain, Dougie 155, 156, 157-8, 159, 160-2, 163, 164

Frodsham 144

Gabriel, David and Liz 77-8, 79, 80-1, 82, 84, 86-7

Gemmill, Toby 82

general practice 133

Golden Lion, Wrington 99-100

Green, Fiona 19-20, 21, 22, 60, 61, 62, 102, 152-65, 188
on the clerking system 24-5
equine clerking rotation 76-82
finals, revision and 154-5, 185
foster practice 155-65
job interview 81, 84, 86-7
surgery clerking rotation 89, 92-3, 94, 95

Green, Graham and Sandra 153, 154

Gregson, Paul 145

guinea pigs 116-17

Harris, Rolf 128

Henry, Bill and Chris 148-50

Herriot, James 20, 65, 128, 141

horses 40-3, 76-87, 135-6
anaesthetising 78, 79
colic 77-80
fitness assessment 76
riggs 90
salmonella virus 82-3

Hughes, Pippa 8, 66, 67, 82, 147

Huxley, John 30-1, 32, 33-4, 35, 43, 44

iguanas 145

injection technique 51

insurance, animal 84

intensive-care facilities 45, 46, 49

job advertisements 149-50, 171-2

jobs market
employment prospects 81-2, 87, 133, 140
general practice 133
industry 133
interview technique 149, 173, 174-5
other career paths 19, 20, 127, 133
PDSA opportunities 111, 112, 119
research 133
RSPCA opportunities 120
salary packages 140, 173, 176
working conditions 119

Johnson, Mark 56

kennels 46

Lane, Dr Geoff 78, 79-80

Langford 7-8, 98-9
commercial activities 9, 29, 68
funding 9

large-animal practice 23-44

Lee, Alison 91, 100-1, 102, 103, 104, 172-8, 175, 188
career goals 173
finals, revision and 100-1, 173, 177, 187
job interview 173, 174-5

Leonard, Steve 17-19, 18, 22, 67, 83, 102, 139, 150-1, 188
dislike of horses 17, 135-6
finals, revision and 185-6
on Kieran O'Brien 17-18, 27

veterinary family background 18, 135, 150-1

VetQuest involvement 133, 134-6

life-and-death decisions 9, 63, 116

lipomas 80

Lloyd, Ruth 110, 111, 112, 118-19

Lynch, Robert 116, 117

mad-cow disease 91

Mason, Lisa 156-8, 159-62, 163-5

milking chamber 8

Milne, Emma 31
RSPCA clerking 121-6

Mostue, Trude 11-12, 13, 21, 22, 56, 73, 101, 165-70, 167, 189
on 'academic cream' tag 11, 15
communication problems 11-12, 38, 73, 74, 170
finals, revision and 180-1, 182-4, 186-7
on Kieran O'Brien 25-6, 36, 38
large-animal clerking rotation 27, 30-4, 36-8
preference for small-animal practice 31, 32, 35
small-animal clerking rotation 46-54, 71-5, 167-70

motivation 19, 130

Noble, Stephanie 47-8, 49, 51, 52-3, 72

Norman, Louise 147

O'Brien, Dr Kieran 19, 25-6, 29, 34, 35-44
on the admissions procedure 16
'bollockings' 26, 27
on examinations 179
on fertility examinations 29-30
hunting pursuits 16-17
on Jon Coupe 16
on Julie Richards 43-4
on Steve Leonard 17
on students' expectations 14-15
students' opinions of 17, 25-6, 36, 38, 101
on students' role at Langford 29

on teaching 35
teaching methods and personality 16, 17, 27
on Trudy Mostue 12, 26, 36
owners, dealing with 47, 108, 110, 116, 118, 149, 174
oxytocin 58

paraclinical subjects 132
Pearson, Professor Harold 88-9, 91, 92, 93-4, 96, 97, 162-3
on the challenges of surgery 91
on examinations 179, 184
retirement 93-4
students' opinions of 89, 101-2
teaching style 89, 92, 94, 162, 163
People's Dispensary for Sick Animals (PDSA) 23, 106-19, 121, 163
personal tutors 48
pet ownership, growth in 45, 119
pets ('companion animals') 45
see also small-animal practice
Pool House Veterinary Hospital 155-62, 163-5
post-mortem room 29
practical experience, gaining 23-4, 120-1
see also clerking rotations
preclinical study 126, 130, 132
presentations 76-7
pressure
examinations 152, 177
of final year 150
performing under 8-9
in the veterinary profession 65
Privett, Rachel 56, 57, 73

rabbits 112, 114-15, 122-5, 146
racehorses 76, 135
rats 108-10, 121-2
rectal vivas 186-7
reptiles 146
Richards, Andrea 140-1
Richards, John and Norma 139, 140, 141
Richards, Julie 38-44, 50, 139-50, 143

finals, revision and 142, 144, 186
foster practice 144-8, 150
large-animal practice clerking 38-44
Ridge, Pat 8, 96, 100, 101, 102, 103, 188
small-animal practice clerking 54-5, 58-64
Robinson, Ken 144-6, 148
Robinson, Sam 56, 57
romantic relationships 104-5, 178
Royal College of Veterinary Surgeons 133
Royal Society for the Prevention of Cruelty to Animals (RSPCA) 23, 88, 119-26, 163

Sandiford, Mike 13, 30, 32, 34, 56, 57, 162, 189
finals, revision and 181, 182, 187
job prospect 181-2
large-animal practice clerking 32, 35-6
PDSA clerking 106, 112, 114-18
School of Medical Sciences 130
schools
and potential veterinary students 19, 127, 141
VetQuest day for sixth-formers 129-36
Scrase, Mrs 112, 114-15
Shaw, Sue 182, 183-4
small-animal hospital 23, 46, 134
small-animal practice 45-75
social life 98-105, 135, 138-9
spaying 88, 91, 92-3
specialisation 34, 133
students
'academic cream' tag 11, 14, 15
accommodation 89, 91
backgrounds 17, 142
camaraderie 177
commitment 20-1
competitive spirit 14-15
debts 97, 173, 174
gender imbalance 102
motivation 19, 130
romantic relationships 104-5, 178
social life 98-105, 135, 138-9

training costs 130, 173
women students 102, 129, 163
surgery 24, 88-97

Taylor, Dr Frank 36
tetanus 26
Thorne, Mike 99-100
tooth trimming 116, 117
Treasure, Glen 122-5, 124
treatment costs 9, 106, 160, 163
Trevett, Julia 185

vacation studies scheme see foster practice
The Vet (BBC TV drama series) 81
vet-school clock tower 47
veterinary practices
bad debts 86
computerisation 86
'everyday' cases 110, 111
recruiting new vets 149-50, 171-2
Veterinary Preclinical School 130
veterinary profession
James Herriot factor 20, 65, 128, 141
service industry 149
stresses in 65
vocational 127
women vets 153
The Veterinary Record 149, 171
VetQuest 129-36
vivas 182-4

Watkins, Liz 175, 176
Williams, Grizelda 120, 121, 122, 125, 126, 127, 128
women vets 153
Wotton, Paul 131
Wray, Jonathan 64, 131
Wright, Carol 96
Wrington 91, 99